Oxford Chemistry S⁻ⁱ

General Editors

P. W. ATKINS   J. S. E. H

G000081045

Oxford Chemistry Series

R. A. Jackson: *Mechanism: an introduction to the study of organic reactions* (1972)

R. J. Puddephatt: *The periodic table of the elements* (1972)

J. Robbins: *Ions in solution (2): an introduction to electrochemistry* (1972)

K. A. McLAUCHLAN
FELLOW OF HERTFORD COLLEGE, OXFORD

Magnetic Resonance

Clarendon Press · Oxford · 1972

Oxford University Press, Ely House, London W.1

GLASGOW NEW YORK TORONTO MELBOURNE WELLINGTON
CAPE TOWN IBADAN NAIROBI DAR ES SALAAM LUSAKA ADDIS ABABA
DELHI BOMBAY CALCUTTA MADRAS KARACHI LAHORE DACCA
KUALA LUMPUR SINGAPORE HONG KONG TOKYO

PRINTED IN GREAT BRITAIN BY
J. W. ARROWSMITH LTD., BRISTOL, ENGLAND

Editor's Foreword

NUCLEAR magnetic resonance has been a dominating structural and analytical tool for several years, and electron spin resonance, while not of such general applicability, has had immense success in the study of the reactions and structure of free radicals. The principles of the two techniques are the same, and the present volume treats them together in order to emphasize their interdependence. The important basic details of the magnetic resonance technique are described and applications to chemical systems are emphasized.

Magnetic resonance is an aspect of the application of magnetism in chemistry, and further information (especially about the magnetic properties of transition-metal complexes) will be found in the later volumes in this series on ligand-field theory and magnetochemistry. Although magnetic resonance is of great importance it might not be the best technique to employ in a particular case: more information on techniques applicable to the study of reaction kinetics will be found in the forthcoming volume on fast reactions. For structural and analytical applications the usefulness of magnetic resonance should be assessed in comparison with diffraction techniques and other forms of molecular spectroscopy, which will be described by later books in the series.

P.W.A.

Preface

So many books have been written about magnetic resonance that this one requires some justification; it is an attempt to provide the undergraduate with a short text which embodies the principles and major applications of both electron spin resonance (e.s.r.) and nuclear magnetic resonance (n.m.r.) and shows their inter-relations. Magnetic resonance is one of the most widely used physical techniques and considerable choice of material has been made; my personal interests and experience inevitably colour this choice and I hope the major faults found with this book will be sins of omission. The text deals simultaneously and equally with the principles and applications of e.s.r. and n.m.r. in the liquid and solid states. The basic phenomena of resonance and relaxation are completely analogous in the two techniques and are treated as such; otherwise, it has long seemed to me that the phenomena of n.m.r. are best approached through their often simpler origins in e.s.r., and that solution effects are incompletely understood without reference to the solid, and conversely. In a short text emphasis inevitably falls on the fundamental interactions which occur but attempt has been made to illustrate their applications with examples chosen from chemistry and biology to indicate the type of problem that magnetic resonance may solve. Magnetic resonance is a continually developing subject and to my personal regret space has allowed no discussion of Fourier transform spectroscopy or of the recent chemically-induced magnetic polarization experiments which allow study of very fast reactions between free radicals (although a reference to the latter is given in the Bibliography).

This text originated in a course given to second-year undergraduates in chemistry at the University of Oxford in 1971; I thank them for their scepticism and helpful criticism. At a more advanced level the phenomena of magnetic resonance are described coherently by the quantum-mechanical perturbation theory approach; here I have tried to explain the physical origins of the interactions observed before quoting the results of the theory. Little recourse to quantum mechanics has been made and a reader familiar with advanced-level G.C.E. physics should be able to follow the text; the quantum theory required for some specific aspects is summarized in Chapter 6 and in the Appendix.

The units used are those of the Système International (SI), since these have positive advantages over c.g.s. units in dealing with the electric and magnetic phenomena of magnetic resonance; the choice causes many equations to take slightly different form from those given in many of the references.

In recent years I have been very fortunate in working in a number of research groups and I thank my colleagues in them for all they have taught me, while absolving them from responsibility for any misconceptions evident in the text. In particular, a great debt is due to Dr. W. J. Dunning, whose insight and enthusiasm first convinced me of the intrinsic interest and philosophy of chemistry; the editor of this book, Dr. P. W. Atkins, has been a continuous source of advice, criticism, and encouragement, for which I am very grateful. Much of the basic planning of the book occurred while I enjoyed the hospitality of the Biochemistry Laboratory of the National Research Council of Canada and I thank my friends there for their stimulating company, particularly Dr. I. C. P. Smith for many interesting discussions. I also thank Howard Coates, Robert Gurd, and Paul Percival for discussing many points with me; Howard also gave great help in running spectra.

Above all, my wife and children have suffered the birth pangs of this book, which my wife has criticized helpfully in the writing; I thank them for their forbearance and patience, confined to Oxford during a wet summer.

K. A. McLAUCHLAN

Acknowledgments

The permission of both authors and publishers to reproduce diagrams from sources listed below is acknowledged gratefully.

Fig. 11, J. Kroh, B. C. Green, and J. W. T. Spinks (1962) *Can. J. Chem.* **40**, 413; Figs 12 and 13, R. O. C. Norman and B. C. Gilbert (1967) *Adv. phys. org. Chem.* **5**, 53, Academic Press; Figs 17 and 46, W. A. Anderson and R. Freeman (1962) *J. chem. Phys.* **37**, 2053; Fig. 27, C. C. McDonald and W. D. Phillips (1967) *J. Am. chem. Soc.* **89**, 6336; Fig. 28, R. J. Abraham and H. J. Bernstein (1961) *Can. J. Chem.* **39**, 216; Fig. 29, C. E. Looney, W. D. Phillips, and E. L. Reilly (1957) *J. Am. chem. Soc.* **79**, 6136; Fig. 32, Z. Luz and S. Meiboom (1964) *J. chem. Phys.* **46**, 1059; Fig. 35, P. B. Ayscough, *Electron spin resonance in chemistry* (1967) Methuen and Co. Ltd.; Fig. 44, R. J. Abraham, R. Freeman, K. A. McLauchlan, and K. G. R. Pachler (1962) *Molec. Phys.* **5**, 321; Fig. 47, L. J. Libertini and O. H. Griffith (1970) *J. chem. Phys.* **53**, 1364; Fig. 49, H. M. McConnell, C. Heller, T. Cole, and R. W. Fessenden (1960) *J. Am. chem. Soc.* **82**, 766; Fig. 50, C. Heller and H. M. McConnell (1960) *J. chem. Phys.* **32**, 1535; Fig. 52, G. E. Pake (1948) *J. chem. Phys.* **16**, 327; Fig. 54, G. Englert and A. Saupe (1964) *Z. Naturf.* **19**A, 172.

Contents

xii   CONTENTS

1. The Principles

Introduction

THE magnetic resonance experiments, electron spin resonance (e.s.r.) and nuclear magnetic resonance (n.m.r.), owe their existence to the property that electrons and certain nuclei possess magnetic moments which interact with applied magnetic fields. These moments result from their having both electrostatic charge and spin angular momentum. The property was known long before the first magnetic resonance experiments were attempted; in the case of the electron from observation of fine structure in atomic spectra, from the anomalous Zeeman effect in atomic spectra, and from the classic Stern–Gerlach experiment in which a beam of S-state silver atoms was split into two separate beams on passage through an inhomogeneous magnetic field; for nuclei the evidence came from the hyperfine structure in atomic spectra although this is not sufficiently large to be resolved for one of the most important magnetic nuclei, hydrogen. For the latter the existence of *ortho* and *para* forms of molecular hydrogen, which differ only in the relative orientations of the vectors representing the spin angular momenta of the nuclei, was deduced from the alternation in intensities of the vibration–rotation bands in its electronic spectrum and from heat capacity measurements.

The fine structure in atomic spectra arises from the interaction between two magnetic fields which both originate in the motion of the electron, one in its orbital motion in the atom and one in its intrinsic spin motion. It is convenient to represent the magnetic properties possessed by virtue of these two types of motion by magnetic dipoles which are vector quantities, with both magnitude and direction, as are the angular momenta in which they originate. (Vectors are represented by characters in bold roman type and their scalar magnitudes by normal roman type.) Let us consider first the magnetic dipole that results from orbital motion; for this we choose some definite physical model and calculate the magnetic moment in terms of the orbital angular momentum. In particular, we suppose that the electron travels in a circular Bohr orbit of radius r with angular velocity $\boldsymbol{\omega}$ such that its angular momentum $\mathbf{l} = I\boldsymbol{\omega} = mr^2\boldsymbol{\omega}$, where I is the moment of inertia of the system and m the electron mass. If t is the time taken to complete a single orbit $|\mathbf{l}| = mr^2 2\pi/t = 2mA/t$, where A is the area of the orbit. Now the circulation of electronic charge $(-e)$ is equivalent to a current $i = -e/t$ flowing in the opposite direction which, by classical electromagnetism, produces a magnetic dipole at the centre of the motion with $\boldsymbol{\mu}_l = A\mathbf{i}$:

$$\boldsymbol{\mu}_l = \frac{-e}{2m}\mathbf{l}. \tag{1}$$

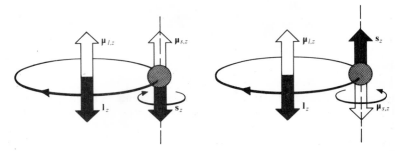

FIG. 1. The configurations of the magnetic moments, arising from the orbital and spin angular momenta of the electron, in the two sublevels.

This important result shows that the vector that represents the magnetic dipole of an electron is collinear with, but opposite in direction to, the angular momentum vector.

The magnetic moment that originates in the spin angular momentum of the electron cannot be calculated in this way for we have no simple physical model of it. The fine structure in atomic spectra can be explained, however, if it is assumed that one-half of the electrons in an atom have magnetic moments that are equal in magnitude, but opposite in sign, to the other half. Pictorially, we may think of the magnetism arising by virtue of charge circulation as the electron rotates about some axis; if it rotates in one direction a certain magnetic moment results but if it rotates in the opposite direction with the same angular momentum an equal but opposite magnetic moment arises. The fine structure results from splitting of the energy levels, which originate in electrostatic interactions between the nucleus and the electrons, by a much smaller magnetic interaction between the orbital and spin magnetic moments. The relative configurations of the moments in two sublevels are shown in Fig. 1 in which s and μ_s represent the spin angular momentum and spin magnetic moment respectively. We shall see in the next section that only the components of both these and the corresponding quantities l and μ_l in some particular direction are defined.

Measurable values of quantum magnetic moments

We have seen that the electron possesses magnetic moments due to its orbital and spin motion and we may ask how to obtain their magnitudes from an experiment. We consider the orbital magnetic moment and, since this is directly proportional to the angular momentum (by equation (1)), we are effectively trying to measure the latter. A convenient property to measure is the energy possessed by a magnetic dipole if it is placed in a magnetic field B:

$$E = -\mu \cdot B. \tag{2}$$

In particular, if the field is applied in the z-direction this has a magnitude $|\mu_{lz}|B_z$. An ordinary bar magnet placed in such a field would simply align with it, but the quantum magnet differs in possessing angular momentum and its resultant motion depends upon the interaction between the couple trying to align it and its inherent angular momentum. The situation is summarized in the vector diagram, Fig. 2. The torque acting on the magnetic moment is $\boldsymbol{\mu}_l \wedge \mathbf{B}$ and by Newton's law this is equal to the rate of change of angular momentum. Changes in $\mathbf{l}$ are therefore perpendicular to both $\boldsymbol{\mu}_l$ and $\mathbf{B}$ and the direction of $\mathbf{l}$ varies rather than its magnitude. The result is that the angular momentum vector, and hence the magnetic moment, precesses about the field direction with a characteristic angular frequency

$$\omega = \frac{\boldsymbol{\mu}_l \cdot \mathbf{B}}{P_l},\qquad(3)$$

where P_l is used to represent the magnitude of the orbital angular momentum (because the symbol l is reserved conventionally for the corresponding quantum number (see below)).

The process, known as Larmor precession, is directly analogous to the motion of a gyroscope under the influence of gravity.

If we measure the energy of the system it is apparent that this depends not upon $\boldsymbol{\mu}_l$ but upon its time-averaged value in the B_z direction, and this is given

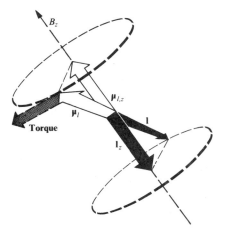

FIG. 2. A vector diagram showing the orbital angular momentum vector $\mathbf{l}$ and the opposite magnetic moment $\boldsymbol{\mu}_l$ in the presence of an applied field B_z; the action of the couple is to cause them to precess about the field direction.

by its projection onto the z-axis, μ_{lz}. Thus, although the magnetic moment has a definite magnitude $|\mu_l|$ there is no experiment which can measure its full value. Furthermore, the components of μ_l in the xy plane change continuously and cannot be measured. The same conclusions are implied for the angular momentum.

This classical model has led to a conclusion of fundamental importance which can be derived rigorously from quantum mechanics which tell us that whereas the total angular momentum of any particle has a magnitude

$$P = \{p(p+1)\}^{\frac{1}{2}}\hbar \tag{4}$$

where p is a quantum number, only certain components of it can be measured, and these have magnitudes, in the z-direction say,

$$P_z = m_p\hbar \tag{5}$$

where $m_p = p, (p-1) \ldots (-p+1), -p$. There are $(2p+1)$ values of m_p. In the case of orbital angular momentum, for example, $P_l = \{l(l+1)\}^{\frac{1}{2}}\hbar$ where l is the orbital angular momentum quantum number and $P_{lz} = m_l\hbar$.

Thus from equation (1) the observable magnetic moment associated with orbital motion in a Bohr orbit $\mu_{lz} = -m_l\,he/2m$. If the electron possesses one quantum of orbital angular momentum μ_{lz} has the magnitude $he/2m$, which is the fundamental unit of magnetism, the Bohr magneton. It is given the symbol μ_B and has a magnitude 9.2737×10^{-20} J G^{-1}.

Combining equations (1) and (3), the Larmor precession frequency

$$\omega = (-e/2m)B_z = \gamma_e B_z, \tag{6}$$

where $\gamma_e = -e/2m$ is a fundamental constant called the *magnetogyric ratio* of the electron. From equation (1), it is simply the proportionality constant between the magnetic moment and the angular momentum from which it results: $\mu_l = \gamma_e l$.

Electron spin angular momentum

Associated with the electron is a spin angular momentum of magnitude $P_s = \{s(s+1)\}^{\frac{1}{2}}\hbar$ which has measurable components $m_s\hbar$. Experiment shows that $s = \frac{1}{2}$ and that $m_s = \pm\frac{1}{2}$ only. In the absence of a physical model of the electron it is tempting to suggest a direct analogy with orbital angular momentum and that the magnetic moment of the electron μ_s should be $\gamma_e s$. However, detailed interpretation of early experimental results showed that the actual magnetic moment appeared to be twice this, a fact that unfairly earned the electron the reputation of having an 'anomalous' magnetic moment. More recent experiments have shown it better to write

$$\mu_s = g_e\gamma_e s = -(g_e\mu_B/\hbar)s, \tag{7}$$

where g_e is a constant called the g-value of the electron and for a free electron has the value 2·0023. (The true spin magnetogyric ratio $\gamma_s = g_e\gamma_e$ by definition.) The origin of this value can be deduced only from advanced theory but the departure from 2·0000 originates in the relativistic correction of the electron velocity. We pause to reflect that this value is obtained from experiments conducted on free electrons, not atoms or molecules.

Nuclear spin angular momentum

Experiment shows that some nuclei, but not all, possess a spin angular momentum of magnitude $P_I = \{I(I+1)\}^{\frac{1}{2}}\hbar$ with observable components $m_I\hbar$. The nuclear spin quantum number, I, is not restricted to $\frac{1}{2}$ but is found to take the values $0, \frac{1}{2}, 1, \frac{3}{2}, 2, \frac{5}{2}, 3, \frac{7}{2}, 4, \frac{9}{2}, 5, 6$, and even $\geqslant 7$, and m_I may take $(2I+1)$ values $(I, I-1, \dots -I+1, -I)$. When discussing magnetic properties it is convenient to define a basic unit of nuclear magnetism, the nuclear magneton $\mu_N = \hbar e/2m_H$, analogous to the Bohr magneton of the electron, where m_H is the mass of the proton, the lightest nucleus to possess spin angular momentum. Its magnitude is 1837 (i.e. m_H/m_e) times smaller than the Bohr magneton.

The magnetic moment of the nucleus is

$$\boldsymbol{\mu}_I = (g_I\mu_N/\hbar)\mathbf{I} = \gamma_I\mathbf{I}, \tag{8}$$

where g_I is the nuclear g-factor, which has the value 5·585 for the proton, and γ_I is the nuclear magnetogyric ratio. Whereas the magnetic moment and spin angular momentum vectors of the electron are necessarily antiparallel there is no such requirement for nuclei, which may possess either positive or negative magnetogyric ratios. Of the familiar nuclei only ^{29}Si, ^{117}Sn, and ^{119}Sn have negative ratios but our knowledge of the nucleus is not yet sufficient to rationalize this. The magnetic moment of the proton is the greatest for all nuclei (except for radioactive tritium) but is much smaller than that of the electron. This is despite the fact that the proton has the smallest nuclear charge and size: a simple physical model such as that used above to indicate the origin of the magnetic moment of the electron would suggest that the magnetic moments of bigger nuclei should be greater.

Our knowledge of nuclear spin quantum numbers rests entirely in experiment although many of them may be rationalized on a very simple theory of the nucleus. Nuclei which contain certain 'magic numbers' of nucleons (protons and neutrons)—2, 8, 20, 28, 50, 82, and 126—are unusually stable, which suggests an analogy with the electronic structures of the inert gases: we postulate that the nucleus contains a series of stationary energy levels. Taking a definite model of the nucleus, one in which the nucleons inhabit a spherical potential well whose potential increases to infinity at the edges, we may calculate these levels and discover that two quantum numbers n and l, which characterize the radial part of the wave function and the orbital angular momentum (within the nucleus) of the nucleon, are required to define them.

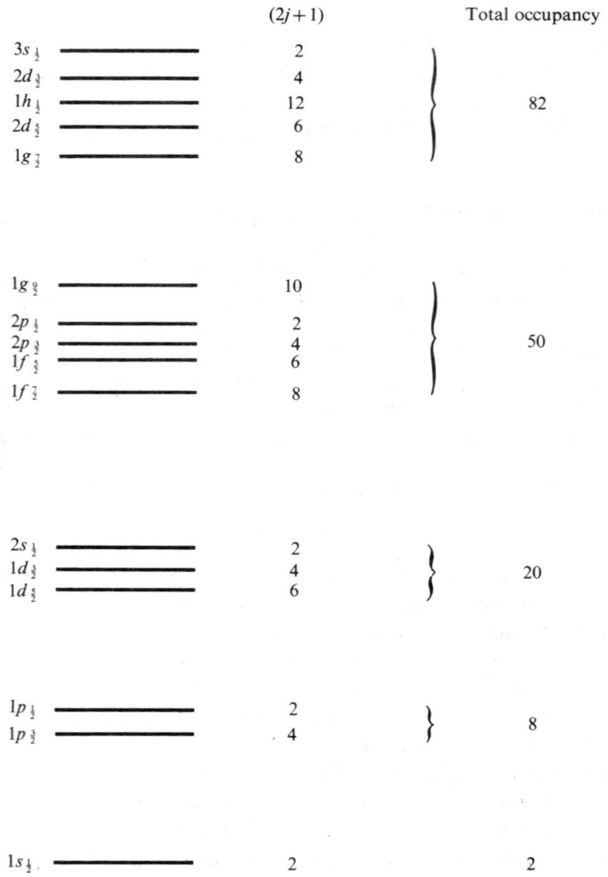

	$(2j+1)$	Total occupancy
$3s_{\frac{1}{2}}$ ─────────	2	
$2d_{\frac{3}{2}}$ ─────────	4	
$1h_{\frac{1}{2}}$ ─────────	12	82
$2d_{\frac{5}{2}}$ ─────────	6	
$1g_{\frac{7}{2}}$ ─────────	8	
$1g_{\frac{9}{2}}$ ─────────	10	
$2p_{\frac{1}{2}}$ ─────────	2	
$2p_{\frac{3}{2}}$ ─────────	4	50
$1f_{\frac{5}{2}}$ ─────────	6	
$1f_{\frac{7}{2}}$ ─────────	8	
$2s_{\frac{1}{2}}$ ─────────	2	
$1d_{\frac{3}{2}}$ ─────────	4	20
$1d_{\frac{5}{2}}$ ─────────	6	
$1p_{\frac{1}{2}}$ ─────────	2	
$1p_{\frac{3}{2}}$ ─────────	4	8
$1s_{\frac{1}{2}}$ ─────────	2	2

FIG. 3. The lower nuclear energy levels available to nucleons; the $(2j+1)$ value gives the occupancy by each type of nucleon.

Furthermore, by analogy with electrons in atoms, we allow spin–orbit coupling between the spin and orbital angular momenta of the protons and of the neutrons (which possess spin angular momentum with quantum number $\frac{1}{2}$) and obtain a resultant angular momentum characterized by a third quantum number j. For each value of l there are $2(2l+1)$ nuclear states (the factor 2 because we are considering both protons and neutrons) and for each value of j, $(2j+1)$ degenerate levels. The energy levels are labelled with n, l, and j values, the l values 0, 1, 2, 3 ... being designated s, p, d, f ... . The lower ones are shown in Fig. 3; they group into five bunches, well separated from each other. Although the nuclear levels containing protons are actually slightly higher than those containing neutrons (owing to electrostatic repulsion) we neglect that fact here. According to the Pauli principle two identical particles of spin quantum number $\frac{1}{2}$ are allowed in each level, and the occupancy of each is equal to the degeneracy for each nucleon (i.e. two protons and two neutrons can each occupy the same non-degenerate level). The occupancy of each level is indicated in the figure as is the progressive total as nucleons are fed in on the 'Aufbau' principle; this rationalizes the 'magic numbers'.

In a particular level the protons pair with antiparallel spins, as do the neutrons, and so those nuclei with even numbers of protons and even numbers of neutrons have zero resultant angular momentum. If a nucleon is unpaired the total angular momentum of the nucleus is given by its j value. For example: ^{1}H, the proton, has a nucleon configuration $(1s_{\frac{1}{2}})^{1}$ and so has a spin quantum number (hereinafter called 'spin') $I = \frac{1}{2}$; ^{13}C has a configuration $(1s_{\frac{1}{2}})^{4}$ $(1p_{\frac{3}{2}})^{8}(1p_{\frac{1}{2}})^{1}$ and has $I = \frac{1}{2}$ also; ^{17}O, with configuration $(1s_{\frac{1}{2}})^{4}(1p_{\frac{3}{2}})^{8}(1p_{\frac{1}{2}})^{4}$ $(1d_{\frac{5}{2}})^{1}$, has $I = \frac{5}{2}$. This simple model sometimes predicts wrong values: for ^{23}Na $I = \frac{5}{2}$ is predicted but $\frac{3}{2}$ is observed. The four stable nuclei ^{2}H, ^{6}Li, ^{10}B, and ^{14}N have odd numbers of both protons and neutrons and do not fit this scheme in which interactions between dissimilar nucleons are not considered.

We summarize our knowledge of nuclear spins as follows.

(1) Nuclei with even charge and mass numbers have $I = 0$ and are non-magnetic. These include the common isotopes ^{16}O and ^{12}C which do not therefore display n.m.r. spectra: a great simplifying feature in the spectra of organic compounds.

(2) Nuclei with odd mass numbers have half-integral spin. These include ^{1}H, ^{19}F, ^{13}C (1·1 per cent naturally abundant) and ^{31}P which have $I = \frac{1}{2}$ and yield high-resolution n.m.r. spectra. Other nuclei have higher half-integral values, for example, ^{59}Co has $I = \frac{7}{2}$.

(3) Nuclei with even mass number and odd charge number have integral spin. Thus ^{2}H has $I = 1$, as does ^{14}N; ^{10}B has $I = 3$. Nuclei with $I > \frac{1}{2}$ are magnetic of course and yield n.m.r. spectra but they also have electric quadrupole moments which complicate their behaviour as compared with $I = \frac{1}{2}$ nuclei. We have no space to discuss these fascinating effects but restrict our detailed discussion to $I = \frac{1}{2}$ nuclei, which allows us to preserve a close analogy with the electron.

Electrons and nuclei in external magnetic fields

A magnetic dipole of moment **μ** placed in a magnetic field **B** experiences an interaction energy given by equation (2). If the field is applied in the z-direction and μ_z is the component of **μ** in this direction, $E = -\mu_z B_z$. The negative sign expresses the greater stability of the dipole within the field. For spin-$\frac{1}{2}$ particles μ_z has either of two values, defined by replacing the full

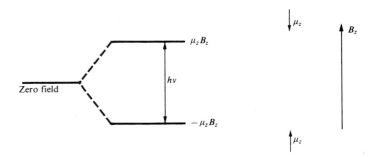

FIG. 4. The removal of the degeneracy of the spin states of spin $\frac{1}{2}$ particles in an applied field; the lowest state of the electron has $m_s = -\frac{1}{2}$ and the proton $m_I = \frac{1}{2}$.

angular momentum vectors in equations (7) and (8) by their observable components, which are opposite in sign and correspond to two different energies: the effect of placing the particle in the field is to remove its spin degeneracy. This is shown schematically in Fig. 4, as are the resolved magnetic moments that correspond to each energy level, with the B_z direction indicated. As in every branch of absorption spectroscopy, we cause transitions between these levels by applying a quantum of energy equal to the energy separation:

$$hv = E_{\text{upper}} - E_{\text{lower}} = 2\mu_z B_z. \qquad (9)$$

Such transitions occur only at the frequency v and we term it a resonant process, the phenomenon being *magnetic resonance*. The resonance condition may be approached either by keeping the field constant and varying the frequency or vice versa, and resonance is detected as an absorption of energy from the applied radiation. The frequency required depends both on the applied field and on the magnetic moment: in the same field the electron requires a higher frequency than does a nucleus. For the electron $|m_s| = \frac{1}{2}$, $|\mu_z| = \frac{1}{2}g_e\mu_B$, and

$$hv = g_e\mu_B B_z. \qquad (10)$$

The choice of the values of field and frequency used in experiment is largely for convenience in using existing electronic equipment: for $B_z = 3\cdot4\,\text{kG}$, $v = 9\cdot5\,\text{GHz}$ ($9\cdot5 \times 10^9\,\text{Hz}$) for the free electron and this is a microwave frequency in the radar X-band. Alternatively Q-band equipment is used at 35 GHz and 12·5 kG. Equation (10) is written in terms of the g-factor rather than the magnetogyric ratio purely by convention whereas the corresponding equation (11) for n.m.r. takes the alternative form. This is largely a historical accident but it reminds us that electrons and nuclei behave quite differently within atoms and molecules. The total angular momentum of the electron

TABLE 1

	Natural abundance (%)	g-value	Magnetogyric ratio (rad $G^{-1} s^{-1}$)	Resonance frequency in a 10 kG field (MHz)
electron	—	2·0023	-1.761×10^7	28,026
^1H	100	5·585	26.752×10^3	42·577
^{13}C	1·1	1·405	6.726×10^3	10·705
^{15}N	0·365	−0·567	-2.712×10^3	4·315
^{19}F	100	5·257	25.167×10^3	40·055
^{29}Si	4·7	−1·111	-5.319×10^3	8·460
^{31}P	100	2·263	10.829×10^3	17·235

may differ from its spin-only value by coupling to the orbital angular momentum to give a resultant $\mathbf{J}$ with an associated magnetic moment $\mu_J = g_J \mu_B \mathbf{J}/\hbar$, where the g-factor normally differs from g_e: g_J should be inserted in equation (10). Nuclei, on the other hand, occupy relatively much smaller volumes of space and have smaller magnetic moments; they couple only weakly to their surroundings and their angular momenta, magnetic moments, and g_I and γ_I values are largely unaffected by the environment. We shall develop these arguments later.

For a spin-$\frac{1}{2}$ nucleus $|m_I| = \frac{1}{2}$, $|\mu_z| = \frac{1}{2}\gamma_I \hbar$ and the n.m.r. resonance condition is $h\nu = \gamma_I \hbar B_z$ or

$$\nu = (\gamma_I/2\pi)B_z. \tag{11}$$

For ^1H, $\gamma_I = 26.7519 \times 10^3$ rad $G^{-1} s^{-1}$ and a number of values of B_z and ν are in use, most commonly 14·1 kG and 23·5 kG at 60 MHz and 100 MHz, respectively, which are convenient radiofrequencies. Other nuclei have distinctly different values of γ_I and at a given magnetic field their resonances occur at quite widely separated frequencies; in any experiment the n.m.r. spectrum of only one of the types of magnetic nucleus present in a molecule is recorded at one time.

The magnetic properties of the electron and some spin-$\frac{1}{2}$ nuclei are given in Table 1.

The vector model of magnetic resonance

Magnetic resonance is simply one aspect of absorption spectroscopy, but whereas in optical spectroscopy illumination is normally of a randomly re-orienting system of molecules in which varying dipole moments interact with light to produce transitions, in magnetic resonance the magnetic moments have definite orientations in space and we inquire how transitions can be induced between the two quantum states. Similar problems arise in infrared spectroscopy, for example, if the spectrum of a molecule oriented inside a crystal lattice is measured: only specific polarizations of the incident light produce transitions. To investigate how to induce magnetic transitions it is convenient to return to the vector model. The two quantum states correspond to two opposite orientations of the magnetic moment vector and each precesses about the field direction as depicted in Fig. 5 (our derivation of precession was for the orbital moment but the same occurs for the spin moment).

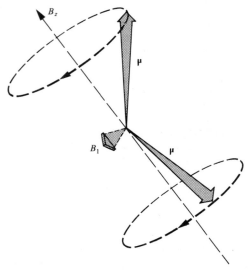

FIG. 5. Precession of the magnetic moment vectors of particles in the two spin states; to induce transitions between the states, B_1 must be perpendicular to B_z but has no effect if it is stationary.

A transition corresponds to the vector passing from one orientation to the other, and to obtain the required torque a magnetic field, $\mathbf{B}_1$, must be applied in a direction perpendicular to B_z. If $\mathbf{B}_1$ is stationary in some particular direction no effective deflection of μ is obtained: when μ has a component along $\mathbf{B}_1$ the vector is tipped away from its normal cone of rotation but when its component is antiparallel to $\mathbf{B}_1$ it is restored to it. To produce a transition $\mathbf{B}_1$ must rotate in phase with the precession of μ that occurs at the Larmor frequency (equation (6)). Thus for resonance it must rotate at an angular frequency $\omega = 2\pi v = \gamma B_z$.

This is just the condition deduced from the quantum model. We shall see precisely how $\mathbf{B}_1$ is applied later.

The ensemble nature of spectroscopy

Whenever we measure the 'spectrum of a molecule' we actually obtain the response from a very large number of similar molecules contained in some sample cell. Thus far we have discussed the properties of individual electrons and nuclei but now we investigate how a large number of them distribute themselves between the two energy states available to spin-$\frac{1}{2}$ particles in an applied field. Providing that the system is in thermal equilibrium with its surroundings we may calculate the distribution from the Boltzmann law. If n_u and n_l are the numbers of particles in the upper and lower levels and T is the absolute temperature,

$$\frac{n_l}{n_u} = \exp\frac{(2\mu_z B_z)}{kT} \approx 1 + \frac{2\mu_z B_z}{kT}, \tag{12}$$

where k is the Boltzmann constant, and we expand the exponential at normal temperatures and fields since the magnetic moments of electrons and nuclei are small. For electrons in a 3·4 kG field the ratio is 1·0025, for ^{1}H at 14·1 kG it is 1·00001, and for all other stable nuclei at the same field even less. Any radiation-induced transition has an equal probability of occurring in absorption or emission and our ability to detect a net absorption of energy at resonance depends upon the excess population in the lower level implied by the minute difference of the ratio from unity: magnetic resonance is inherently an insensitive technique. Nuclear magnetic resonance observations on weak solutions or uncommon nuclei require highly sophisticated detection methods and the populations are made as different as possible by working in the highest available homogeneous fields, currently 70·5 kG (this also facilitates interpretation of the spectrum, see later); e.s.r. is more sensitive and fortunately X-band apparatus has sufficient sensitivity for most purposes since microwave technology at much higher frequencies is not well developed. The population difference implies that a sample possesses a bulk static magnetic susceptibility and this may be detected with difficulty.

Spin relaxation

When radiation induces transitions between the states the Boltzmann populations are disturbed; at equilibrium the greater number of particles is in the lower state and at resonance initially more upward transitions occur than downward ones: we expect the populations to equalize rapidly. When they become equal there is no resultant absorption of energy and although magnetic resonance transitions occur they cannot be detected: this is termed *saturation* and is observed if high-power levels of radiation are applied. The fact that magnetic resonance can be observed while radiation is applied at low-power levels implies that there occur other non-radiative 'relaxation' processes which oppose saturation and attempt to restore the Boltzmann population difference. The same problem exists in other fields of spectroscopy but is accentuated in magnetic resonance which has the smallest quantum of energy and population difference; in optical spectroscopy spontaneous emission from the upper level is more probable (in ^{1}H n.m.r. it occurs once in 10^{18} years) and the relaxation processes are more efficient.

We think of a spin system that has absorbed energy as having increased its temperature, and the relaxation process is simply its method of re-attaining thermal equilibrium with its surroundings. This is known as *spin-lattice relaxation*, where 'lattice' simply implies 'surroundings' which may be gas, liquid, or solid. The mechanism is simple: throughout the sample all spin-$\frac{1}{2}$ particles have magnetic moments which produce local magnetic fields in the space surrounding them with which the magnetic moment of another particle may interact. In a liquid, for example, these fields constantly fluctuate as a result of molecular buffeting in the Brownian motion; if a fluctuation occurs at the resonance frequency it may induce a transition quite independent of the applied radiation.

The nature of the effect is easy to calculate if we use radiation to disturb equilibrium but then remove it. Let the probabilities per unit time of upward and downward relaxation transitions be w_1 and w_2 and define $N = (n_1 + n_u)$ and $n = (n_1 - n_u)$; $dn_1/dt = (n_u w_2 - n_1 w_1)$ and $dn_u/dt = (n_1 w_1 - n_u w_2)$.

$$\frac{dn}{dt} = 2w_2 n_u - 2w_1 n_1 = N(w_2 - w_1) - n(w_2 + w_1), \tag{13}$$

or

$$\frac{dn}{dt} = \frac{n_0 - n}{T_1}, \tag{14}$$

where

$$n_0 = N\frac{(w_2 - w_1)}{(w_2 + w_1)} \quad \text{and} \quad \frac{1}{T_1} = (w_1 + w_2).$$

Hence $n = n_0 + c\,e^{-t/T_1}$, where c is an integration constant and n_0 is the population difference at thermal equilibrium. A more convenient form of this equation is

$$n - n_0 = (n - n_0)_0\, e^{-t/T_1}, \tag{15}$$

where $(n - n_0)_0$ represents the disturbance from the thermal equilibrium population difference at $t = 0$. This equation shows that following a disturbance the population difference, and hence the bulk magnetization of the sample, returns to its equilibrium value exponentially with a characteristic time T_1, known as the *spin-lattice relaxation time*. The complete behaviour of the spin system in a normal magnetic resonance experiment can be described by including a term for the rate of radiation-induced transitions in equation

(13); the equation above applies specifically to pulse experiments in which the radiation is removed immediately it has upset the equilibrium population difference.

In normal liquids T_1 is much shorter for electrons than for nuclei since their greater magnetic moments interact more strongly with the surroundings. With the origin of spin-lattice relaxation lying in the motion of the surroundings, T_1 may be very long in solids at low temperatures, even several years in magnetically dilute ones. This precluded success when the n.m.r. experiment was attempted first in 1936 on a solid whose T_1 is now known to be long and whose resonance therefore saturated.

The widths of magnetic resonance transitions

The width of any spectroscopic line depends upon the precision to which the energies of the levels between which the transition occurs are defined. In magnetic resonance this depends both on the lifetimes of particles in the states and on local magnetic field inhomogeneities. From the Uncertainty Principle, the uncertainty in the energy of a level, ΔE, is related to the lifetime Δt through the relation $\Delta E \Delta t \geqslant \hbar$ and the line-width, which is the uncertainty Δv of a transition occurring between two levels in which we assume the particles to have similar lifetime is $\Delta v \geqslant 1/\pi \Delta t$.

If the lifetime is controlled by spin-lattice relaxation the line-width is inversely proportional to T_1 but in practice this is rarely so since there exist other factors which control the lifetime or which broaden the lines by purely magnetic effects; the fundamental effects concerned are called *spin–spin relaxation processes* and are characterized by a relaxation time T_2. In liquids the two effects share a common origin, which is also common to spin-lattice relaxation, in the magnetic field that surrounds a magnetic dipole of moment μ. At a distance r from the dipole, with an angle θ between the dipole axis and the distance vector, this field has a magnitude

$$B_{\text{dipolar}} = \frac{\mu_0}{4\pi} \frac{\mu_z}{r^3}(3\cos^2\theta - 1), \tag{16}$$

where μ_0 is the permeability of space and in the presence of a strong applied field only μ_z is defined. Spin-lattice relaxation is caused by the component of this field which fluctuates at the resonance frequency due to variations in r and θ caused by Brownian motion. If one spin-$\frac{1}{2}$ particle undergoes a transition from one spin state to the other the local field surrounding it changes at the precise resonance frequency and may cause a transition of a second particle which interacts with it. By conservation of energy the two particles undergo transition in opposite directions so that the relative spin populations of the energy levels are unaffected and this is not a spin-lattice relaxation process. However, the lifetime of the particles in each level is affected and leads to lifetime broadening of the line—a spin–spin relaxation process. In a liquid,

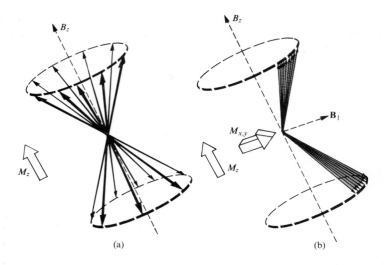

FIG. 6. (a) Precession of an ensemble of vectors with random phase in the x- and y-directions produces a non-zero magnetization in the z-direction only. (b) Application of a $\mathbf{B}_1$ field, which rotates at the resonance frequency, causes the vectors to attain phase coherence and yields a magnetization in the xy-plane. This diagram is drawn in a rotating frame of axes and shows $\mathbf{B}_1$ stationary.

molecules are in random motion and the time-averaged value of the dipolar field is zero since $\overline{\cos^2\theta} = \frac{1}{3}$. At any instant, however, it is not zero, and different particles in the sample experience slightly different resultant local magnetic fields (the sum of B_z and B_{dipolar}) and the spin states of some particles are separated by greater energies than are others: instead of one resonance condition there are many close in frequency and the spectral line is broadened: again this is a spin–spin relaxation process.

It is surprising at first sight that these two processes are characterized by a single relaxation time T_2 but this follows from the vector model of an ensemble of moments and is summarized in Fig. 6: in the absence of a $\mathbf{B}_1$ field the individual moments precess with random phase about the z-(field) direction but there is a greater number in the lower energy state and the system has an initial magnetization M_z; in the perpendicular directions both M_x and M_y average to zero. If a $\mathbf{B}_1$ field is applied at the precise Larmor frequency we may draw the result in a system of coordinates that rotates at this frequency and therefore shows $\mathbf{B}_1$ as stationary: the effect is to deflect all the moments in the $\mathbf{B}_1$ direction and, while M_z decreases due to transitions, M_x and M_y become non-zero as the moments attain phase coherence. On removing the $\mathbf{B}_1$ field M_z returns to its initial value by spin lattice relaxation, but M_x and M_y change in quite a different manner: any process that removes the phase coherence decreases their values. The two processes of spin–spin relaxation do precisely this: from equations (2) and (3) it is seen that the precession frequency depends on the energy of the moment in the field; any uncertainty in the energy implies that a range of such frequencies exist, while the instantaneous dipolar fields cause the precise precession frequencies of all the moments to differ. The magnetization in the xy plane therefore varies (also exponentially) with a single characteristic time. On this model T_1 characterizes the return of the magnetization to its equilibrium value in the field direction and T_2 the return to zero in the perpendicular directions: they are sometimes known as the *longitudinal* and *transverse* relaxation times.

The study of relaxation effects is an intriguing field of magnetic resonance, for it tells us of the motion of the surroundings of the magnetic particles, but here we note only a few general features. Most importantly, relaxation controls the widths of resonance lines: in solution these normally have a Lorentzian shape whereas in solids they are Gaussian.† In solution n.m.r. lines are displayed as normal absorption curves, but in solids the derivative of the curve with respect to field is measured, as it is for all e.s.r. lines (see last section). The width of solution n.m.r. lines at half-maximum height is $(1/\pi T_2)$ Hz and the separation between the peaks of the derivative curve of solution e.s.r. lines is $(\pi T_2/\sqrt{3})$ Hz; in solids the corresponding separation is $(1/\pi T_2)$ Hz. These formulae allow measurement of T_2.

In normal liquids T_1 and T_2 are often equal although this depends inherently on molecular motion. In a solid at low temperatures T_1 may be long but T_2, through its now static term in the dipolar field, short; the magnetic resonance line is broad. Between the liquid and the solid there is a gradation in behaviour which, for example, causes T_1 and T_2 to differ in viscous liquids. In liquid systems that display e.s.r. spectra both T_1 and T_2 are very short (about 10^{-6} s) and the lines are again broad (about 0·1 MHz). The nuclear relaxation times in liquids are, however, long (1–50 s for ^{1}H) and the lines are consequently sharp: so sharp that their width (about 0·3 Hz) is determined usually by applied field inhomogeneities rather than by true relaxation processes.

Systems that have magnetic resonance spectra

Any stable molecule that contains magnetic nuclei has an n.m.r. spectrum. Such a molecule does not have an e.s.r. spectrum, however, since in each molecular orbital electrons exist in pairs with anti-parallel spins and therefore they possess zero net spin magnetic moments (although if the orbital has angular momentum the molecule may possess a non-zero magnetic moment; this could be detected in a beam experiment but the transitions involved are

† For a line centred at a frequency v^*, a Lorentzian line-shape is described by the equation $f(v) = 2T_2\{1 + 4\pi^2 T_2^2(v - v^*)^2\}^{-1}$, and a Gaussian line-shape by the equation $f(v) = 2^{\frac{1}{2}}\pi^{\frac{1}{2}}T_2 \exp\{-2\pi^2 T_2^2(v - v^*)^2\}$.

not in the appropriate frequency range to be detected in a normal e.s.r. experiment). E.s.r. spectra can be observed only from species that contain unpaired electrons (usually in their ground states); these include atoms, inorganic and organic free radicals, and the ions of transition metals, rare earths, and trans-uranic elements. Some of these are highly reactive and require special experimental techniques to be observed. Magnetic resonance spectra can be detected in the gas, liquid, and solid phases, although comparatively little work has been performed on gases.

Experimental aspects

A magnetic resonance spectrometer requires a magnetic field, a source of radiation, a sample, and a detector. The resonance condition can be reached either by keeping the radiation frequency constant and sweeping the field, or conversely; in e.s.r. the field is invariably swept but in n.m.r. both methods are in common use.

The simplest n.m.r. spectrometer, shown in Fig. 7, consists of a radio-frequency bridge in which the sample is contained, inside the magnetic field, in one arm; initially the bridge is balanced but as the field is swept through resonance the sample absorbs energy and the bridge is unbalanced. The radio-frequency signal which results is detected and rectified by standard radio-frequency methods. The field B_1 required to induce transitions must be applied perpendicularly to the main magnetic field and must rotate at the resonance frequency, or at least should have a component which is circularly polarized. This is attained by applying plane-polarized electromagnetic radiation in such a direction as to have a circularly polarized magnetic component in the appropriate plane (a sinusoidally varying plane polarized wave may be considered to be composed of two counter-rotating circularly polarized magnetic components in a plane perpendicular to its direction of propagation; the component that rotates in the same direction as the spin precession induces the transition). The radiation source is a transmitter whose frequency is crystal controlled, and radiation is applied to the sample, contained in a cylindrical glass tube, by means of a coil wound along the tube axis at right angles to the main field. The sharpness of n.m.r. lines in solution (less than 0·05 mG) places extreme requirements on the stability of the transmitter and the stability and homogeneity of the applied field (in modern instruments the ratio of the field and frequency is actually maintained constant). To attain sufficient homogeneity many techniques are used. The sample, of typical volume 0·4 ml, is contained in a thin-walled glass tube selected to be free of inhomogeneities; this tube is rotated at about 30 Hz about its vertical axis by an air turbine, which has the effect of averaging out the different magnetic fields that might be expected at different parts of the sample as a result of field gradients in the directions perpendicular to the tube axis. The magnet, particularly its pole pieces, is manufactured from special alloys of small grain

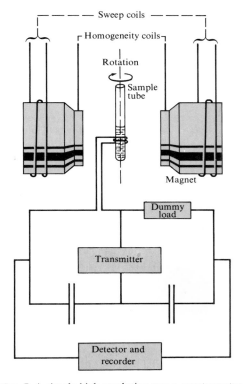

Sweep coils

Homogeneity coils

Rotation

Sample
tube

Magnet

Dummy
load

Transmitter

Detector and
recorder

FIG. 7. A simple high-resolution n.m.r. spectrometer.

size, and 'field homogeneity coils' are wound onto the pole faces. These are electrical coils through which small currents are passed to produce small changes of field at the sample, an empirical procedure which is performed to optimize homogeneity each time a spectrometer is used. The incremental fields produced amount to a few milligauss at maximum and the field sweep range of a high-resolution spectrometer operated to observe ^{1}H spectra at 14·1 kG is only about 1 G. At best fields homogeneous to one part in 10^9 are obtained. Whether the spectrum is displayed by sweeping the field or the frequency, it is always calibrated in frequency units (Hz).

The same basic spectrometer may be used to observe n.m.r. spectra of solids although the lines may be several gauss wide; the field must be swept over hundreds of gauss and the stability and homogeneity of frequency and field no longer are critical. (A similar situation pertains in e.s.r. spectroscopy although the lines in solution may be only a few milligauss in width.) With

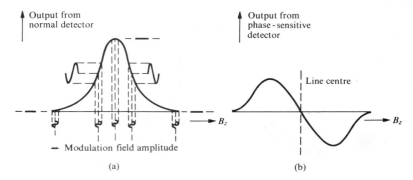

FIG. 8. The effect of modulating the magnetic field and detecting at the modulation frequency is to convert the normal signal (a) to its derivative (b); in (a) it can be seen that the modulated output from the detector varies in amplitude and in phase as the field modulation is experienced at different parts of the normal signal when the total field is swept.

broad lines an addition to the spectrometer becomes of advantage: around the sample cell is wound a further set of coils through which an alternating current is applied to produce a small field at the sample which varies sinusoidally with time; this is known as *field modulation*. The current is so adjusted that the maximum variation in the field at the sample is much less than the width of its resonance line; as the system is swept through resonance the output from the detector also varies at the modulation frequency, as shown in Fig. 8. The output, whose magnitude depends on the slope of the normal signal at the point where the modulation is applied, is passed to a phase-sensitive detector which is fed with the modulation frequency as a reference (the arrangement is included in the e.s.r. spectrometer shown in Fig. 9); this detector passes and rectifies only that part of the input signal which varies at the reference frequency and rejects all others. The advantage of this system is that whereas in normal detectors all frequencies contribute to the electrical noise of the output, here only those components of the noise in the input which occur at the reference frequency are detected: a considerable gain in signal-to-noise ratio ensues. As its name implies, the output from the detector depends on the phase of the input signal and since it also depends upon the slope of the normal line it constitutes the derivative of the original: the line centre is where it crosses the field axis. If the modulation field is set too high considerable distortion, known as *modulation broadening* of the output, occurs; its avoidance is essential to the observation of true line shapes and is particularly important in observing e.s.r. lines in solution.

The e.s.r. spectrometer is similar to the n.m.r. one in principle (it too has a bridge circuit) but not in appearance. The microwave frequencies required are obtained from klystron oscillators and are fed to the sample, not along coaxial wires, which have very low impedance to earth at these frequencies, but along wave-guides. These are hollow metal pipes of rectangular cross-section whose inside surfaces are preferably gold-plated and whose dimensions depend critically on the wavelength of the radiation which is simply reflected down them off the inside surfaces; for X-band radiation (of 3-cm wavelength) the internal dimensions are 2·3 cm by 1 cm. A common type of spectrometer containing a 'magic tee' bridge is shown in Fig. 9. In this, one half of the radiation from the klystron enters a cavity containing the sample and, off resonance, is reflected back from it into the bridge where it is balanced by the other half. At resonance, energy absorption by the sample unbalances the bridge, and microwave radiation falls onto a semiconducting crystal detector which rectifies it. The samples are held within a resonant cavity in which

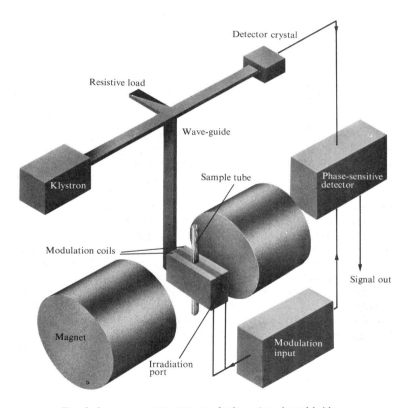

FIG. 9. An e.s.r. spectrometer employing a 'magic tee' bridge.

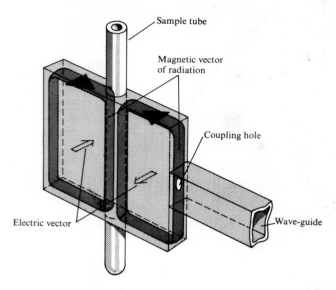

Sample tube

Magnetic vector
of radiation

Coupling hole

Wave-guide

Electric vector

FIG. 10. A microwave cavity, showing the spatial separation of the magnetic and electric vectors of the standing wave.

standing waves are set up by reflections off the end walls when radiation is fed in through a small coupling hole from the wave-guide; the cavity serves to concentrate the magnetic field at the sample and ensures that it has a component suitable for inducing transitions. One such cavity is shown in Fig. 10. An important feature is that the regions of maximum electric and magnetic field are well separated in space. This is useful since *aqueous* solutions exhibit considerable dielectric loss at these frequencies which prevents the establishment of the standing wave pattern; by containing them in flat sample cells in which the solution is held in the nodal plane of the electric field this problem is overcome. For solvents other than water, sample cells are cylindrical, contain roughly 1-ml samples of liquid, and are of quartz since Pyrex glass normally contains paramagnetic impurities which yield their own e.s.r. response.

Modern spectrometers are highly sophisticated and any full description would require much space; we have described just those features essential to the experiment and to understanding the phenomena that are observed.

2. Spectra from Liquids

IN n.m.r. the appearance of spectra from liquid samples differs enormously from those from solids, and so does the information obtained from them; in e.s.r. the difference, although less marked, is still considerable. Here we describe the general features of solution spectra and in succeeding chapters we shall discuss the origins of the effects we encounter. There are many similarities between e.s.r. and n.m.r. spectra but there exists a basic difference in that whereas most molecules contain more than one magnetic nucleus few radicals contain more than one unpaired electron; metal ions often do, so do triplet species, and their e.s.r. spectra will be discussed briefly later.

Electron spin resonance spectra

The e.s.r. spectrum of a radical that contains no magnetic nuclei, such as the anion SO_3^-, consists of a single line; if its centre is at a field $B_z(i)$ we consider it to have a g-value g_i given by the resonance condition $hv = g_i\mu_B B_z(i)$. If magnetic nuclei are present the spectrum often consists of more than one line and is said to exhibit hyperfine structure. The spectrum of hydrogen atoms, produced for example by electron irradiation of liquid hydrocarbons at low temperature through a hole in the side of the cavity, consists of two equally intense lines 506·8 G apart (Fig. 11(a)); the g-value is calculated from the mean field of the two lines. The electron and the nucleus are said to be *coupled* and the separation of the two lines is the *hyperfine coupling constant*, A, which we define as having frequency units ($A_H = 1420·4\,\text{MHz}$). If deuterated hydrocarbons are irradiated a symmetric triplet spectrum of equally intense lines from deuterium atoms is observed (Fig. 11(b)). Here $A_D = 218·2\,\text{MHz}$ and we note that $A_H/A_D = 6·51 = \gamma_H/\gamma_D$, which suggests that the mechanism of the coupling involves magnetic interactions between the electron and the nucleus. Furthermore, the hydrogen nucleus has two possible projections of its magnetic moment in the applied field (corresponding to $m_I = \pm\frac{1}{2}$), while the deuterium nucleus of spin 1 has three ($m_I = 0, \pm 1$): the e.s.r. line is split into $(2I+1)$ components. These facts are consistent with an interaction whose energy depends upon the relative orientations of the magnetic moments, and consequently the angular momenta, of the particles; that is, whose energy is proportional to $\mathbf{s}.\mathbf{I}$: in the applied field m_I has $(2I+1)$ possible values and m_S two ($2S+1 = 2$), which correspond to the upper and lower spin states of the electron. Each electron energy level is therefore split into $(2I+1)$ sublevels and as the selection rules for the transitions are $m_s = \pm 1$ and $m_I = 0$, then $(2I+1)$ transitions are expected. In Chapter 6 it will be shown that the magnitudes of the splittings are rationalized with an interaction $(4\pi^2 A/h)\mathbf{s}.\mathbf{I}$.

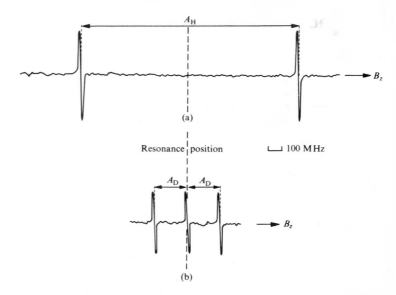

FIG. 11. The e.s.r. spectra of (a) hydrogen atoms and (b) deuterium atoms. These spectra have been reconstructed from real spectra obtained with the species trapped in frozen soiutions at low temperatures; the published true solution spectra show intensity anomalies (see P. W. Atkins and K. A. McLauchlan in the Bibliography).

Most radicals contain more than one magnetic nucleus and in favourable circumstances each couples to the electron to produce splittings in the spectrum. The methyl radical, produced by one of the methods listed below, contains three equivalent hydrogens and its spectrum (Fig. 12(a)) consists of four lines of equal spacing ($A_{Me} = 64\cdot4$ MHz) with intensities in the ratio $1:3:3:1$. These observations are simply rationalized by adding the splittings produced by each equivalent nucleus in turn (Fig. 12(b)): in general the e.s.r. spectrum of an electron coupled to n equivalent spin-$\frac{1}{2}$ nuclei consists of $(n+1)$ lines whose relative intensities are given by the coefficients of the binomial expansion of $(1+x)^n$. Spectra that obey this rule are termed *first-order*. Most e.s.r. spectra in solution are of this type at normal spectrometer frequencies and both g and A may be measured directly from them.

If the radical is not symmetric the electron couples to different extents with different nuclei. For example, the radical $\cdot CH_2OH$ has a spectrum (Fig. 13) in which each line of the triplet due to coupling to the equivalent methylene protons is further split into a doublet by coupling to the hydroxyl one. In general, coupling constants vary in a consistent fashion along a saturated hydrocarbon chain; with the electron localized at the α-carbon atom average

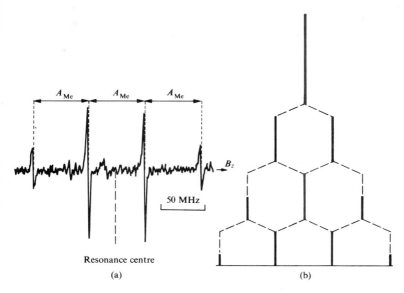

FIG. 12. (a) The e.s.r. spectrum of methyl radicals in aqueous solution, with two weak lines from a second radical. (b) The $1:3:3:1$ quartet pattern is rationalized by adding the identical splittings of three equivalent protons.

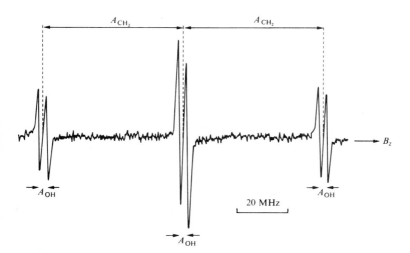

FIG. 13. The e.s.r. spectrum of $\cdot CH_2OH$.

values of hyperfine coupling constants to protons attached to α-, β-, and γ-carbons are 61·6 MHz, 84 MHz, and 1·4 MHz respectively. No coupling is observed to protons further down the chain. The values are affected by substitution, particularly if a double bond is introduced: in the $CH_2=CH\cdot$ radical $A_\alpha = 44$ MHz and $A_\beta = 144$ MHz. The coupling is sensitive therefore to the structure of the radical and allows the radical present in solution to be identified: the multiplicity of the lines yields the number of protons that couple and the magnitudes of the splittings indicate their positions in the radical relative to a localized electron. This is a major application of e.s.r.

The highly reactive species investigated require special techniques for their production and observation. In solution, radical anions of aromatic molecules can be produced either by reduction of the parent molecule with an electropositive metal in dimethoxy-ethane or tetrahydrofuran solution, or by electrolytic reduction; in the absence of oxygen they are stable. Neutral radicals are observed usually in steady-state concentrations in which they are continuously produced to replenish those lost by reaction. Direct radiolysis inside the cavity has proved very useful but in photolysis it is usual to produce radicals by reaction from primary species formed on light absorption. These include the $\cdot$OH radical from photolysis of H_2O_2 added in about 1 per cent concentration, for example:

$$\cdot OH + CH_3OH \rightarrow \cdot CH_2OH + H_2O,$$

and triplet molecules from irradiation of organic aldehydes and ketones which yield radicals by hydrogen abstraction from the solvent:

$$(C_6H_5CHO)^T + \text{solvent} \rightarrow C_6H_5(HO)CH\cdot + \text{solvent radical}.$$

Alternatively, primary radicals may be formed, rapidly flowed into the cavity, and reacted there with a substrate molecule that flows in by a different path:

$$Ti^{3+} + H_2O_2 \rightarrow \cdot OH + OH^- + Ti^{4+},$$

$$\cdot OH + C_6H_6 \rightarrow \cdot C_6H_6OH, \text{hydroxyphenyl}.$$

Very recently, pulse radiolysis and flash photolysis have been used to observe radicals only 10^{-6} s after formation; these experiments, which require special instrumentation, are unique in their ability to identify transient radicals in solution.

Nuclear magnetic resonance spectra

The principles that affect the appearance of spectra for all spin-$\frac{1}{2}$ nuclei are embodied in ^1H spectra, which will be discussed specifically; owing to the extreme narrowness of the lines they are termed *high-resolution spectra*.

A sample containing equimolar quantities of benzene and cyclohexane has the spectrum illustrated in Fig. 14. It consists of two lines, and from their

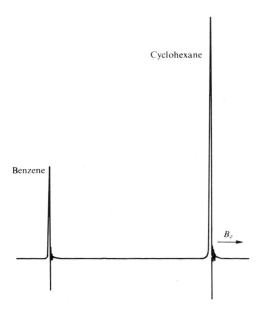

Cyclohexane

Benzene

B_z

FIG. 14. The 60 MHz n.m.r. spectrum of an equimolar mixture of benzene and cyclohexane, showing the phenomenon of 'ringing' which distorts the signal in the direction of the sweep.

intensities we deduce that the line at the lower magnetic field arises from the benzene protons while the other arises from cyclohexane, which contains twice as many protons per molecule. (Whether the spectrum is displayed by sweeping the field or the frequency it is always depicted as a field sweep with the field increasing from left to right.) The experimental observation is that magnetic nuclei in different chemical environments exhibit resonance at different values of the applied field, a conclusion of great implication to the chemist. The lines are distorted on the side in the direction of the sweep by 'ringing', a common artifact produced by sweeping the resonance more quickly than theoretically desirable. Its observation in spectra is useful in adjusting the homogeneity of the applied field since the ringing decays exponentially with a homogeneity controlled 'relaxation time'. Otherwise it contains no information useful to the chemist and can be eliminated by sweeping each resonance in a time that is long compared with its T_2 value.

The resonances in Fig. 14 are said to be separated by a *chemical shift*, which is found to vary with the total applied field of the spectrometer in a linear fashion: in a 20 kG field it is exactly twice that in a 10 kG field. It appears that the field actually experienced by a nucleus in a molecule differs from the applied one, the discrepancy being directly proportional to the field strength. This is the result of the applied field inducing a circulation of electrons in the molecule which, by Lenz's law of electromagnetism, occurs in such a direction as to induce a magnetic field which opposes the applied one. If B_{local} and B_{ind} are the actual and induced fields at a nucleus, $B_{local} = B_z - B_{ind}$; by Lenz's law $B_{ind} = \sigma B_z$ where σ is a constant of proportionality, the *screening constant*. Hence $B_{local} = B_z(1-\sigma)$ and at resonance

$$v = \frac{\gamma}{2\pi}B_{local} = \frac{\gamma}{2\pi}B_z(1-\sigma). \tag{17}$$

In one chemical environment the electron density surrounding a nucleus is different from that in another and so the magnitudes of the induced fields, and σ-values, differ. For two nuclei, i and j,

$$v_i - v_j = \frac{\gamma B_z}{2\pi}(\sigma_j - \sigma_i) = v_0(\sigma_j - \sigma_i), \tag{18}$$

where v_0 is the spectrometer frequency; the nuclei may be in the same or different molecules. In a given field the absolute value of the resonance frequency of a nucleus is characteristic of its precise environment: simply by measuring the n.m.r. spectrum of a molecule the identity of each type of proton it contains can, in principle, be obtained. For example, an aldehyde proton has a different resonance frequency from a methyl proton, the precise values even depending upon the groups to which they are attached.

Absolute frequency measurements to sufficient accuracy (0·3 Hz in 10^8 Hz) are difficult in practice and it is more convenient to measure relative frequencies: an inert substance is added to the sample and its resonance is used as a reference from which all others are measured. In non-aqueous solvents tetramethylsilane, $(CH_3)_4Si$, is used as the internal reference and yields a strong signal to high field of most other lines; in water a related compound, $(CH_3)_3SiCH_2CH_2CH_2SO_3Na$ is used, whose methyl resonance differs negligibly from that of tetramethylsilane (T.M.S.). The total spread of a proton spectrum is normally about 1 kHz and to attain sufficient measurement precision an accuracy of only 3 in 10^4 is required. All other nuclei have larger chemical shifts; for instance, the spread in ^{13}C spectra is 30 kHz.

Since the chemical shift depends upon the field at which the spectrometer operates, information obtained at one field can be useful at another only if it is suitably scaled. This is a problem of considerable importance as technological innovation constantly increases the operating fields of spectrometers, and so we define a dimensionless chemical shift

$$\delta_{ij} = (v_i - v_j)/v_{ij}, \tag{19}$$

where v_{ij} is the mean resonance frequency; in practice it can be replaced by

v_0, without loss of accuracy since $v_0 \approx v_{ij} \gg (v_i - v_j)$. The denominator is of the order of 100 MHz and the numerator 1 kHz; to avoid inconvenience δ is expressed in parts per million (p.p.m.): it is normally in the range 0–10 p.p.m. With T.M.S. as a reference, we define shifts $\delta_i = (v_{T.M.S.} - v_i)/v_0$ p.p.m. and this implies $\delta_{T.M.S.}$ is zero. This is the basis of the 'δ-scale' of chemical shifts in which δ-values increase from zero in the low-field direction (an alternative scale, the τ-scale, has T.M.S. at 10.00τ : $\tau_i = 10 - \delta_i$; resonances from nuclei which experience a large screening effect, σ, have small δ-values but large τ-values).

From the above it is apparent that $|\delta_i| = |(\sigma_{T.M.S.} - \sigma_i)|$. Resonances that fall near to that of T.M.S. have similar screening constants; those at high δ-values occur to low field of T.M.S. and the nuclei are said to be *deshielded* with respect to those at higher field which are more *shielded*. This nomenclature may be understood by reference to equation (17): at a given frequency a large σ-value, which results from the nucleus being 'shielded' from the applied field by a high local electron density, implies that B_z must be changed by a greater amount to produce resonance than if σ is small. In general, resonances at low field are those in which the group containing the nucleus is attached to an electron-withdrawing substituent; the δ-values of the methyl halides are CH_3F : 4·26, CH_3Cl : 3·05, CH_3Br : 2·68, CH_3I : 2·16, the order expected from the relative electronegativities of the halogens. The origins of chemical shifts

TABLE 2

Some representative chemical shift values

Compound	δ-value	Compound	δ-value
acetic acid (acid proton)	11·37	acetaldehyde	
acetaldehyde		(methyl protons)	2·20
(aldehyde proton)	9·80	acetone	2·17
benzene	7·37	methyl cyanide	2·00
chloroform	7·27	acetylene	1·49
trichloroethylene	6·45	cyclohexane	1·43
ethylene	5·32	ethane	0·89
methylene dichloride	5·30	methane	0·14
dioxan	3·57		

	Some methyl shifts in CH_3X		
X	δ-value	X	δ-value
C_6H_5COO	3·90	$COCH_3$	2·17
C_6H_5O	3·73	$COOCH_3$	2·00
OH	3·38	CH_2Br	1·65
OCH_3	3·24	$C(CH_3)_3$	0·94
C_6H_5	2·32	$Si(CH_3)_3$	0·00

are, however, complex and multitudinous (Chapter 4). Some δ-values for common groups are summarized in Table 2, which also contains a series of values for methyl groups attached to different substituents. Solvents used in n.m.r. must be chosen with care, otherwise their resonances obscure those of interest; fully deuterated ones are commonly used.

When magnetic nuclei are present in the same molecule the spectrum is often more complex and each resonance may be split. The spectrum of a molecule which contains two inequivalent nuclei, dichloro-acetaldehyde $CHCl_2CHO$, is shown in Fig. 15. It consists of two equal doublets of equal intensity and of small splitting, separated by a much greater splitting; the chemical shift of each nucleus is measured from the centre of each doublet and the assignments of the resonances to specific nuclei in the molecule are made by comparison with literature values for nuclei in known environments. The magnitude of the doublet splitting is much less than the chemical shift between the nuclei and, in contrast to the chemical shift, does not vary if the applied field is changed. In a way analogous to e.s.r., we say that the nuclei are *spin–spin coupled* together with a coupling constant J, defined so as to have frequency units. The splitting, which in this simple case is a direct measure of the coupling constant, is the same in each resonance: this is a diagnostic test by which nuclei that couple may be identified in a spectrum.

The chemical shift is not always large compared with the coupling constant; when it is (by a factor of 10, for example), n.m.r. spectra obey precisely the same 'first-order' rules as do e.s.r. spectra: the resonance of a spin-$\frac{1}{2}$ nucleus which couples to another of spin I is split into $(2I + 1)$ lines; equal coupling to n equivalent spin-$\frac{1}{2}$ nuclei results in $(n + 1)$ lines with intensity ratios corresponding to the coefficients in the binomial expansion. Spectra that involve coupling of two nuclei of differing magnetogyric ratios, for example ^{31}P and ^{19}F spectra from PF_3, invariably obey these rules at normal operating field strengths. The basis of spin–spin splitting is similar to that of hyperfine coupling in e.s.r. and originates in magnetic interaction between nuclei i and j of magnitude $(4\pi^2 J/h)\mathbf{I}_i \cdot \mathbf{I}_j$: $\mathbf{I}_i$ and $\mathbf{I}_j$ have $(2I_i + 1)$ and $(2I_j + 1)$ components in the direction of the applied field, giving $(2I_i + 1)(2I_j + 1)$ energy levels. With selection rules for the transitions of nucleus i, $\Delta m_i = \pm 1$, $\Delta m_j = 0$, and similarly for j, it is

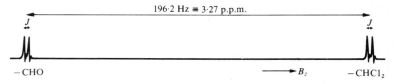

FIG. 15. The 60 MHz n.m.r. spectrum of dichloroacetaldehyde showing splitting due to spin–spin coupling; the chemical shifts are too large to show the resonance of the reference compound T.M.S. on the same diagram. It occurs to high field.

predicted that $(2I_j + 1)$ transitions occur for i and $(2I_i + 1)$ for j. For $I_i = I_j = \frac{1}{2}$, there are two of each.

Knowing that nuclei in a molecule may couple together it is surprising to find that the spectrum of methyl iodide, for example, is a single line; the protons do couple but the coupling fails to produce splitting since it happens

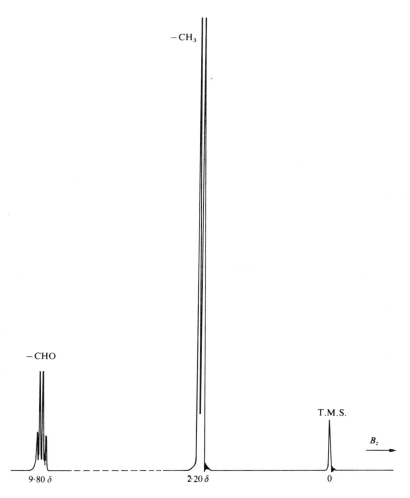

FIG. 16. The 60 MHz n.m.r. spectrum of acetaldehyde, with T.M.S. added as a reference compound.

that all the transitions occur at the same frequency. This phenomenon occurs always if two or more nuclei have the same chemical shift.

The spectra of more complex molecules are easily interpreted if they are 'first order'. Thus the 60 MHz spectrum of acetaldehyde (Fig. 16) consists of a quartet at low field, with a $1:3:3:1$ intensity distribution, and a doublet at high field. The assignments are made from inspection of the total signal intensities. The more intense peak (at $2 \cdot 20 \delta$) is thus due to the methyl group. The doublet originates in coupling to the single aldehyde proton (the coupling of the methyl protons to each other is not observed); the quartet and its intensities may be rationalized by adding successive identical splittings from the three equivalent hydrogens in the methyl group, just as was done in the e.s.r. spectrum of the methyl radical. As a rule of thumb, each group may be thought of as sensing the resultant spin states of the other: the methyl group senses the $m_I = \pm\frac{1}{2}$ states of the aldehyde proton and is split into a doublet; the aldehyde proton senses the four possible resultant spin states of the methyl group, $m_I = \frac{3}{2}, \frac{1}{2}, -\frac{1}{2}, -\frac{3}{2}$ and is split into a quartet. Moreover, whereas the $\pm\frac{3}{2}$ states can be obtained in only one configuration of the individual spins, for example $(+\frac{1}{2}, +\frac{1}{2}, +\frac{1}{2})$, the $\pm\frac{1}{2}$ ones can be obtained in three, for example $(+\frac{1}{2}+\frac{1}{2}-\frac{1}{2})$, $(+\frac{1}{2}-\frac{1}{2}+\frac{1}{2})$, and $(-\frac{1}{2}+\frac{1}{2}+\frac{1}{2})$ (where it is implied that we can distinguish the m_I value of each proton); this rationalizes the intensity distribution. Any one nucleus may couple to however many others are close enough to do so; the effect is simply additive.

In 'first-order' cases chemical shifts and coupling constants are measured directly from spectra; unfortunately the majority of spectra that involve coupling of nuclei with the same magnetogyric ratios are not of this type. For instance, the 60 MHz spectrum of a second molecule which contains just two inequivalent protons, 2-bromo-5-chlorothiophene, is shown in Fig. 17. In the *special case* of two nuclei the coupling constant can still be measured directly as the separation of the weak lines from their neighbouring strong ones, but

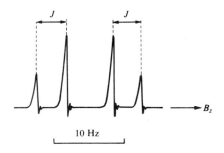

FIG. 17. The 60 MHz n.m.r. spectrum of 2-bromo-5-chlorothiophene showing departure from the 'first-order' rules.

the chemical shift must be computed by the methods of Chapter 6. Often, however, accurate values are not necessary to assign the lines in a spectrum to individual nuclei in a molecule and much chemistry can be accomplished without them. The appearance of a spectrum depends upon the ratios of the chemical shifts of the nuclei to the coupling constants between them; as these decrease the intensities of the lines are affected initially but the splittings change little; when the ratios are smaller still the intensity distortions increase, the splittings change, and the multiplicity rules break down. Since the chemical shift is field-dependent the spectrum of a molecule may be quite different if obtained at two different field strengths; no analogous effect exists in optical spectroscopy.

The fine structure of n.m.r. spectra has similar application to hyperfine structure in e.s.r. but is of wider use since diamagnetic materials are more common than paramagnetic ones. In ^1H spectra J lies in the range -20 to $+40$ Hz but is usually 0–10 Hz; in saturated hydrocarbons, spin–spin coupling attenuates rapidly down the chain: coupling occurs between nuclei attached to the same carbon atom and to the adjacent one but all couplings over greater distances are zero. The values are affected by substitution and unsaturation, in the presence of which coupling may occur between nuclei several bonds apart, as in *trans* crotonaldehyde $CH_3CH=CHCHO$, in which the *cis* olefinic proton couples to the methyl group.

Nuclear magnetic resonance spectroscopy gives the chemist a remarkably full picture of a molecule. He deduces the precise environments of the nuclei from their chemical shifts and their relative amounts from their intensities; the multiplicities of the resonances allow deduction of the numbers of nuclei that couple; the magnitudes of the splittings reveal whether the protons are attached to the same or adjacent (for saturated compounds) carbon atoms. Later it will be seen that the magnitudes may also indicate the relative configurations of the atoms, that is their stereochemistry, and also the conformations of cyclic molecules. Despite all this information it is usually not possible to deduce a unique structure of a molecule from its high-resolution n.m.r. spectrum: n.m.r. should be considered as complementary to optical spectroscopic and mass spectrometric methods of structure determination. Finally, we should note the comparative simplicity of magnetic resonance spectra; high resolution (gas phase) investigation of the optical spectra of any of the molecules or radicals whose spectra are shown in this chapter shows them to consist of thousands of transitions. The n.m.r. and e.s.r. spectra owe their simplicity to the fortunate coincidence that the normal isotopes of carbon and oxygen have no magnetic moments.

The two principal factors that determine the appearance of magnetic resonance spectra may be summarized. First, the centres of the spectra occur in different places for different species because of differences in g-value (in e.s.r.) and chemical shift (in n.m.r.); both, as we shall see, depend upon the generation of an induced electron circulation by the applied field. The multiplet structure in magnetic resonance spectra (hyperfine structure in e.s.r., fine structure in n.m.r. and triplet state e.s.r. (see Chapter 7)) arises from magnetic coupling of the particles: electron–nucleus coupling is the origin of hyperfine structure in e.s.r., nucleus–nucleus coupling yields the fine structure in n.m.r. spectra, and electron–electron coupling yields the fine structure in the e.s.r. spectra of triplet species. These are the fundamental properties of magnetic resonance; their connection with molecular structure is discussed in the chapters that follow.

3. The *g*-Factor

IT was stated in Chapter 1 that the g-value of an electron may differ from its free spin value of 2·0023 whenever the electron forms part of an atomic system in which it possesses orbital angular momentum. This effect is investigated in this chapter which, notwithstanding our introduction to the g-value as an experimental measurable in liquids in Chapter 2, is concerned with the origins and implications of the effects that cause g to differ from 2·0023 in all three phases of matter. Initially we consider the gaseous atom, and proceed thence to molecules and crystals.

The gaseous atom

We consider a polyelectron atom in which the electrons possess net spin and orbital angular momenta and in which the magnetic interactions between their magnetic moments and the applied field are small compared with the electrostatic interactions in the atom. This situation gives rise to 'Russell–Saunders' coupling in which all the individual orbital angular momenta of the electrons couple together to give a resultant $\mathbf{L}$, as do the spin ones to give $\mathbf{S}$. Symbolically, $\mathbf{L} = \sum_i \mathbf{l}_i$, with magnitude $P_L = \{L(L+1)\}^{\frac{1}{2}}\hbar$; similarly $\mathbf{S} = \sum_i \mathbf{s}_i$, with magnitude $P_S = \{S(S+1)\}^{\frac{1}{2}}\hbar$. The total angular momentum $\mathbf{J}$, of magnitude $\{J(J+1)\}^{\frac{1}{2}}\hbar$, is the resultant of $\mathbf{L}$ and $\mathbf{S}$ and we calculate the magnetic moment $\boldsymbol{\mu}_J$ associated with it; this is simple from the vector diagram, Fig. 18. In this diagram both angular momentum and magnetic moment vectors are drawn and it must be remembered that the spin magnetic moment vector is proportionately twice as large as the spin angular momentum vector. The effect is that the resultant magnetic moment vector $\boldsymbol{\mu}_{LS}$ is not collinear with $\mathbf{J}$ and consequently precesses about it; the magnetic moment $\boldsymbol{\mu}_J$ is the time average of $\boldsymbol{\mu}_{LS}$ over the precession, that is its projection in the J direction:

$$\boldsymbol{\mu}_J = -\boldsymbol{\mu}_L \cos\theta - \boldsymbol{\mu}_S \cos\phi$$

$$= -e/2m(\mathbf{L}\cos\theta + 2\mathbf{S}\cos\phi).$$

Cos θ and cos ϕ can be evaluated from the cosine law to give

$$\mu_J = \frac{-e}{2m}\left(\frac{3P_J^2 - P_L^2 + P_S^2}{2P_J}\right).$$

But $\mu_J = -g_J\mu_B P_J/\hbar = -g_J P_J e/2m$. Comparing these equations and evaluating the momenta,

$$g_J = 1 + \frac{J(J+1) - L(L+1) + S(S+1)}{2J(J+1)}. \tag{20}$$

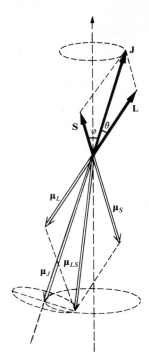

FIG. 18. Vector addition of the resultant magnetic moment vectors due to orbital and spin motion yields a resultant $\mathbf{\mu}_{LS}$ which is not collinear with the resultant angular momentum vector $\mathbf{J}$ and precesses about it; its component in the $\mathbf{J}$ direction is $\mathbf{\mu}_J$.

This is known as the Landé splitting factor and allows variations of the g-value between 0 and 2·0. When $L = 0$, $g_J = 2$ and when $L \gg S$, $g_J \sim 1$: the effect of the orbital angular momentum is to reduce the g-value. It will be seen below that similar effects occur in radicals in which $g_J \sim 2$ if the orbital angular momentum makes little contribution and g_J differs from 2 if it does, often to lower values but sometimes to higher ones.

In gaseous diatomic radicals the rotational angular momentum couples also to give a resultant $\mathbf{F}$; for ClO for example the ground state has $F = \frac{3}{2}$ and, on applying a magnetic field $(2F + 1) = 4$, non-degenerate energy levels are obtained between which three transitions may be induced, the separations of which allow the moment of inertia of the molecule to be calculated, and hence its bond distance. The transitions are not pure e.s.r. ones for the energy level differences are not purely magnetic in origin.

Spin–orbit coupling

We have seen that the coupling of the spin and orbital angular momenta of an electron is paramount in determining its g-value. The energy of the interaction we define as $(4\pi^2\zeta/h)\mathbf{L}.\mathbf{S}$ where ζ is the spin–orbit coupling constant and has frequency units, and we consider the factors that control its magnitude. We use a simple model in which the magnetic moment $\boldsymbol{\mu}_S$ is considered to interact with a magnetic field $\mathbf{B}_L$ which the electron experiences from its orbital motion with a velocity $\mathbf{v}$ in the electrostatic field $\mathbf{E}$ of the nucleus: we equate $-\boldsymbol{\mu}_S.\mathbf{B}_L$ to the coupling energy.

From classical electromagnetism $\mathbf{B}_L = \mathbf{E} \wedge \mathbf{v}/c^2$. $\mathbf{E}$ originates in a potential field $V(r)$ which is a function of the distance r from the nucleus: $\mathbf{E} = -(\mathbf{r}/r)\,\mathrm{d}V(r)/\mathrm{d}r$ and

$$\mathbf{B}_L = -\frac{\mathbf{r} \wedge \mathbf{v}}{rc^2}\frac{\mathrm{d}V(r)}{\mathrm{d}r} = -\frac{\mathbf{L}}{mrc^2}\frac{\mathrm{d}V(r)}{\mathrm{d}r}.$$

For a spherical atom of nuclear charge Ze, $V(r) = Ze/4\pi\varepsilon_0 r$, where ε_0 is the permittivity of space, and

$$\mathbf{B}_L = -\frac{Ze}{4\pi\varepsilon_0 mc^2}\frac{\mathbf{L}}{r^3}.$$

This derivation has treated the relative motion of the electron and nucleus non-relativistically: a proper relativistic treatment halves the value. We require the average value of $\mathbf{B}_L$ as the electron moves around the nucleus.

$$-\boldsymbol{\mu}_S.\mathbf{B}_L = \frac{Ze^2}{8\pi\varepsilon_0 m^2 c^2}\left(\overline{\frac{1}{r^3}}\right)\mathbf{L}.\mathbf{S},$$

where we have taken $g_e = 2$ and the bar denotes an average ('expectation') value.

Hence

$$\zeta = \frac{Ze^2 h}{32\pi^3 \varepsilon_0 m^2 c^2}\left(\overline{\frac{1}{r^3}}\right).$$

The average value of the inverse cube of the distance is simply calculated if the atomic wave functions are known. For the hydrogen atom

$$\left(\overline{\frac{1}{r^3}}\right) = \frac{Z^3}{a_0^3 n^3 l(l+1)(l+2)},$$

where n and l are the usual quantum numbers and a_0 is the Bohr radius (5.29167×10^{-11} m). We see that $\zeta \propto Z^4$ and, although the calculation has been performed for hydrogen with $Z = 1$, the dependence on a high power of Z is found for all atoms: spin–orbit coupling becomes rapidly more effective as the atomic number increases.

The quenching of orbital angular momentum

From the above it appears that the g-values of free radicals and ions should differ widely from g_e but experiment shows that those of organic radicals and of ions of the first row of the transition series (unless they are in spherically symmetric environments) differ little from 2·0023, while inorganic radicals show a slightly larger variation than do organic radicals. The observations are consistent with the orbital angular momentum making little or no contribution to the total magnetic moment and it is said to be *quenched*. The phenomenon was first recognized in measurements of the static magnetic susceptibilities of compounds of transition metal ions. A crude physical picture of the origin of quenching is that the electron in its random motion inside an orbital is only likely to travel in one direction as often as it does in the opposite direction, and its average angular momentum is zero. A quantum mechanical calculation of this average or 'expectation' value confirms that it is zero provided that the orbital is non-degenerate. It is important to realize that this conclusion is independent of the presence of an applied field. The reason why the orbital angular momentum may be quenched when an atom or ion forms part of a molecule or crystal, whereas it is not in the free species, lies in the removal of orbital degeneracies through interaction with intense local electric

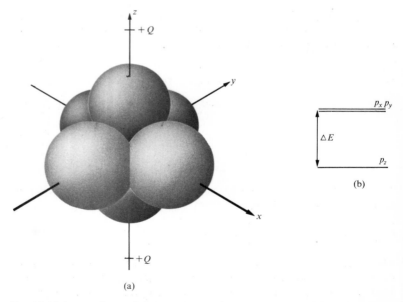

FIG. 19. (a) An atomic set of three p-orbitals oriented inside a ligand field represented by positive charges on the z-axis. (b) The effect on the energy levels of the orbitals.

fields due to surrounding nuclei and electrons. In the crystal the field is the well-known ligand field.

A simple system to consider is the effect on the energies of three initially degenerate p-orbitals in an atom of a pair of electric charges placed symmetrically about the nucleus (Fig. 19(a)). The presence of the positive charges decreases the energy of the p_z-orbital relative to the energies of the p_x- and p_y-orbitals, which to a first approximation are unaffected (Fig. 19(b)). If the atom contains a single electron in the p-shell, it enters the lowest orbital, p_z, which is non-degenerate and its orbital angular momentum is quenched. In general, ligand-field symmetries are such that the degeneracy of the p_x- and p_y-orbitals is removed also. Whenever the local electric field is such that the lowest level is degenerate the electron has a non-zero average orbital angular momentum which contributes to its magnetic moment; this occurs in symmetric systems such as linear radicals and ions in sufficiently symmetric environments.

The electron has no electric dipole moment and its spin angular momentum is consequently unaffected by an electric field: its contribution to the g-factor remains inside a molecule or crystal.

The g-factor in molecules and crystals

We have seen that the g-factor may or may not depend upon contributions from the orbital angular momentum and the problem arises of how the resonance condition, equation (7), should be rewritten to account for this. For convenience we retain the same general form and write, as in Chapter 2, $h\nu = g_i\mu_B B_z(i)$; that is, we retain the Bohr magneton and use the single factor g_i to describe deviation from free-electron behaviour. This equation may be rewritten as $h\nu = g_e\mu_B(g_i B_z(i)/g_e)$; that is, the electron can be thought of as moving in an effective magnetic field $(g_i B_z(i)/g_e)$ with its spin-only magnetic moment $\frac{1}{2}g_e\mu_B$; this is exactly analogous to the approach taken to describe the chemical shifts in n.m.r. in Chapter 2. Henceforth we omit the i from subscripts and parentheses and simply use g to imply a value differing from g_e.

The energy of the electron in a field B_z has a magnitude

$$\tfrac{1}{2}g\mu_B B_z = \tfrac{1}{2}g_e\mu_B B_z + \tfrac{1}{2}\delta g\mu_B B_z,$$

where $g = g_e + \delta g$. The first term on the right-hand side of this equation represents the energy of a free electron in a field B_z, and we wish to discover the origin of the second term. We may think of it as the energy possessed by the electron as a result of it having acquired extra spin angular momentum and therefore an extra magnetic moment $\frac{1}{2}\delta g\mu_B$; it can do this through spin–orbit coupling by which any orbital angular momentum may communicate spin momentum to the electron, the effect depending on the energy $(4\pi^2\zeta/h)\mathbf{L}\cdot\mathbf{S}$. As we have seen, quenching in molecules may cause the resultant value of $\mathbf{L}$ to be zero; however in the presence of an applied magnetic field an orbital circulation of electrons is induced, just as described in explaining chemical shifts in n.m.r. By Lenz's law the motion occurs in such a direction as to induce a magnetic field which tends to oppose the applied one; the circulation is in a plane perpendicular to the applied field. Clearly the effect on the spin angular momentum depends both on the magnitude of the induced orbital motion and on the spin–orbit coupling constant: it is greatest for heavy atoms.

In our previous model of partially degenerate p-orbitals in the presence of an electric field we saw that the electron occupies the lowest, p_z, orbital in which it has zero average angular momentum and nor can a magnetic field applied in the z-direction induce any: in this direction δg is zero and $g_{zz} = g_e$. A magnetic field applied in the x-direction tends to induce the electron to circulate in the perpendicular plane, yz. In the absence of a field such circulation could occur only by excitation of the electron from the p_z- to the p_y- orbital (if the orbitals had been degenerate this circulation could occur without excitation); the effect of the field is to induce circulation without excitation although the ease with which it occurs depends inversely on the energy separation of the unperturbed states. In the language of quantum mechanics we say that the wave functions of the two states are mixed by the applied field and the effect on the g-value can be calculated using second-order perturbation theory (Appendix), which yields

$$\delta g = -\frac{16\pi^2\zeta}{\hbar} \sum_n \frac{\langle\psi_0|\hat{\mathbf{l}}|\psi_n\rangle\langle\psi_n|\hat{\mathbf{l}}|\psi_0\rangle}{E_n - E_0}. \tag{21}$$

The symbolism is explained in the Appendix; $\hat{\mathbf{l}}$ is the orbital angular momentum operator, summation is over all excited states of the radical, and $(E_n - E_0)$ represents the energy between an excited state ψ_n and the ground state ψ_0. Evaluation of this equation using hydrogen p-orbital wave functions gives

$$g_{xx} = g_{yy} = g_e - 8\pi^2\zeta\hbar/\Delta E.$$

The important conclusion is that the g-value of a radical or ion oriented in space, for example inside a crystal, depends upon the direction along which it is measured; it is anisotropic. It is in fact a tensor† quantity with nine components which may be written as a matrix. If the matrix is diagonal only the three principal values need be quoted, and these three values (g_{xx}, g_{yy}, and g_{zz}) may be interpreted as the g- values along the x-, y-, and z-axes of the radical.

---

† A vector quantity has but three components and a change in one produces no change in the orthogonal ones; a tensor allows such a change or a change in any other direction. For example, on stretching, a piece of elastic is elongated in length but contracted in diameter; such a process is described by a tensor. In a molecule the electrons are constrained largely in volumes closely associated with chemical bonds: the effect of an applied field on their orbital angular momenta reflects this constraint and it may produce changes in the momenta, and g-values at various angles with respect to its direction.

The double suffix notation is necessary to define all nine components, off-diagonal ones having values such as g_{xy} and g_{xz}.

In a normal liquid a radical undergoes rapid reorientation under Brownian motion and an average value $g = \frac{1}{3}(g_{xx} + g_{yy} + g_{zz})$ is observed. In crystals, on the other hand, the field can be applied in some definite direction: if X_x, X_y, and X_z are the cosines of the angles between the applied field and the x-, y-, and z-axes of the tensor, the observed value at any angle $g = (g_{xx}^2 X_x^2 + g_{yy}^2 X_y^2 + g_{zz}^2 X_z^2)^{\frac{1}{2}}$, and the principal components may be obtained by measuring g at different angles. In general, the principal axes of the g-tensor do not coincide with the crystal axes and the measurements, made typically by varying the angles between the field and the crystal axes, allow the relative orientations of the two sets of axes to be determined. If the symmetry of the g-tensor in the molecular framework is obvious, the crystal structure may be deduced. In a polycrystalline solid, such as a powder, the spectrum is the envelope of the spectra from all possible orientations of the radical or ion but the principal components of the g-factor may be measured directly from it; in Fig. 20(a) is shown the spectrum which results if the tensor is axially symmetric ($g_{xx} = g_{yy} \equiv g_\perp$; $g_{zz} \equiv g_\parallel$) and in Fig. 20(b) if it is anisotropic (with $g_{xx} > g_{yy} > g_{zz}$).

Although we have indicated the origins of g-values in an atomic system the model is relevant to molecules also: the molecular orbital wave function may be written as a linear combination of those of the individual atoms that comprise the molecule,

$$\Psi_{\text{M.O.}} = c_1\psi_1 + c_2\psi_2 + c_3\psi_3 + \dots + c_n\psi_n, \tag{22}$$

where $c_1, c_2, \dots, c_n$ are constant coefficients, and inserting molecular wave functions into equation (21) and expanding the matrix elements yields terms in the mixing of all pairs of atomic orbitals, although the equation needs to be re-cast slightly to allow different spin–orbit coupling constants on different atoms. The magnitude of δg still depends upon the individual constants ζ of

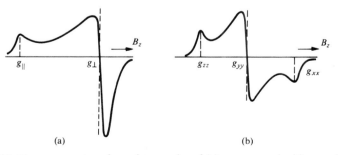

FIG. 20. The e.s.r. spectra of powder samples of (a) a compound with an axially-symmetric g-tensor and (b) a compound with an anisotropic one.

different atoms. These calculations involve summing over all excited states, whose wave functions and energies are rarely known. If one particular excited state is close in energy to the ground state its effect may be dominant. On this assumption δg need be evaluated only over this and the ground state and the expression contains the coefficients of the atomic orbitals in just these two states. If the wave function of one of the states can be calculated, measurement of δg allows that of the other to be deduced. This is possible only for simple radicals, such as the isoelectronic pair CO_2^- and NO_2 in which the nature of the upper state is calculable and the orbital occupied by the unpaired electron can be deduced; a good qualitative understanding of its nature is obtained.

In transition metal ions the unpaired electron occupies a d-orbital, the precise one depending upon the ligand-field splittings in its crystalline environment and therefore on the symmetry of the environment. The spin–orbit coupling is large at the ion and contributions from the ligand atoms are negligible. The ligand field may be sufficiently asymmetric to remove the degeneracy of the d-orbitals almost completely although Kramer's theorem states that in the absence of an external magnetic field the electronic states of any molecule which contains an odd number of electrons are at least doubly degenerate. The calculation of the g-values introduces no new principles although now d-orbital wave functions and their energy separations are required. Analysis of observed g-values allows estimation of the energy gaps,

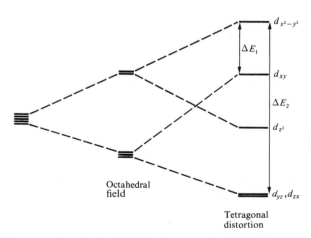

FIG. 21. The energy levels of a Cu(II) ion in an octahedral ligand field which has tetragonal distortion. The unpaired electron of this d^9 complex occupies the uppermost level.

if the spin–orbit coupling constant is known. In Cu(II) complexes, for example, the Jahn–Teller effect causes a strong distortion of the basic octahedral geometry to tetragonal and the degeneracy of the d-orbitals is largely removed (Fig. 21). The single unpaired electron in this $3d^9$ ion occupies the highest orbital, $d_{x^2-y^2}$, and its wave function can mix with others of appropriate symmetry under the influence of the applied magnetic field: either d_{xy} or d_{yz} (or the degenerate d_{zx} one). Theoretical analysis shows that

$$g_\parallel = g_e + 32\pi^2 \zeta h k_1 / \Delta E_1 \quad \text{and} \quad g_\perp = g_e + 8\pi^2 \zeta h k_2 / \Delta E_2,$$

where $k_1 + k_2 = 1$ if the complex is completely ionic (k_1 and k_2 may be regarded as measures of the degree of covalent bonding). For $Cu^{2+}(H_2O)_6$, $g_\parallel = 2.397$, $g_\perp = 2.083$, $\Delta E = \frac{1}{2}(\Delta E_1 + \Delta E_2) = 13\,500\,\text{cm}^{-1}$, $k_1 = 0.85$, and $k_2 = 1.0$. For $Cu^{2+}(H_2O)_2(\text{acetylacetonate})_2$, $g_\parallel = 2.266$, $g_\perp = 2.053$, $\Delta E = 15\,000\,\text{cm}^{-1}$, $k_1 = 0.75$, and $k_2 = 0.87$.

Observed values of g-factors

In gaseous atoms and diatomic radicals the net effect of spin–orbit coupling is to reduce the g-values: when $s = \frac{1}{2}$ they fall in the range $0 - g_e$. For atoms the values are known very accurately from beam experiments: for ^{1}H g is 2.00226, for ^{19}F 1.333861, and for ^{127}I 1.333995; for the radical ClO it is 0.799. These low values imply that high values of the applied field are required to observe their e.s.r. spectra at X-band: 8.6 kG for ClO.

The g-values observed for organic radicals are almost isotropic and differ only slightly from g_e. For example, $\cdot$CH$_3$ has $g = 2.00255$, $\cdot$CH$_2$CH$_3$ 2.0026; $\cdot$CH$_2$OH 2.0033; $\cdot$C(OH)(CH$_3$)$_2$ 2.0031; $\cdot$CH$_2$CHO 2.0045, and $\cdot$CH$_2$-COCH$_3$ 2.0042. These values show that the hydrocarbon radical value is altered by characteristic amounts by α-substitution with hydroxyl and carbonyl groups, the result of spin–orbit coupling to the hetero atom. If the electron is localized on an atom other than carbon the deviations from g_e increase, also because of increased spin–orbit coupling: nitroxide radicals $R_2\dot{N}O$ have $g \approx 2.006$ and peroxide radicals $ROO\cdot$, 2.015. For the same reason, inorganic radicals show larger deviations from g_e and are often anisotropic: the azide ion N_3^- has components 1.984, 2.001, and 2.001; nitrogen dioxide has values 2.0062, 1.9910, and 2.0020; the SO_3^- ion has a value 2.004, which is isotropic. Although these deviations from g_e are small, g-values can be measured to ± 0.0001 and can be used to some extent as diagnostic tests for structure, just like the chemical shifts in n.m.r. In practice the hyperfine structure is usually more useful for this purpose and g-values are used only to resolve situations in which two or more different radicals may exhibit similar hyperfine structure or where the radical shows no hyperfine structure.

The transition metals of the first row have their unpaired electrons in their outermost shells where they are most likely to interact with their environment:

the orbital angular momentum is quenched and the g-values differ little from g_e. For example, the $3d^3$ ions, V^{2+}, Cr^{3+}, and Mn^{4+}, have nearly isotropic values in the range 1·98–1·99; the $3d^5$ ions Fe^{3+}, Mn^{2+}, and Cr^+ have almost isotropic values close to 2·00; the $3d^8$ and $3d^9$ ions show larger deviations: Ni^{2+} has almost isotropic g-values of around 2·25, and Cu^{2+} has anisotropic g-values 2·1–2·4. In general, the g-values observed for an ion depend on its precise environment and vary from one compound to another.

When the unpaired electrons occupy inner electron shells the orbital angular momentum is by no means fully quenched and very large deviations of g from g_e occur, with correspondingly large anisotropies. This is the situation which pertains in the rare-earth series. Some of these ions, Gd^{3+} and Eu^{2+}, have S-ground states, and therefore zero orbital momentum, and isotropic g-values around 2·00. Ions containing an odd number of electrons, Ce^{3+}, Nd^{3+}, Sm^{3+}, Dy^{3+}, Er^{3+}, Yb^{3+}, have g-values in the range 0·25–9·0. For example, Ce^{3+} has a cylindrically symmetric g-tensor: in cerium nitrate $g_{\parallel} = 0.25$, $g_{\perp} = 1.84$, while in a calcium fluoride host lattice $g_{\parallel} = 3.038$ and $g_{\perp} = 1.396$. For Dy^{3+} in its nitrate $g_{\parallel} = 4.28$, $g_{\perp} = 8.92$. Ions with an even number of electrons show greater deviations still: Pr^{3+} in a lanthanum chloride lattice has $g_{\parallel} = 1.035$, $g_{\perp} = 0.10$; Ho^{3+} in the same lattice has $g_{\parallel} = 16.01$, $g_{\perp} = 0$. These wide variations in g-values require very large field sweeps to be observed.

4. The Chemical Shift

CHEMICAL shifts arise from screening constant differences which have origins similar to g-value variations in paramagnetic systems. However, convention requires us to treat electrons and nuclei in molecules in different ways: whereas the magnetic moment of the electron is considered to depend upon its surroundings, nuclear magnetic moments are treated as invariant. The perturbations of the electron orbital momentum that occur when an atom or molecule is placed in an applied field are thought of as affecting the local field at the nucleus; we now calculate this field in an atom.

The atom

We consider an isolated atom with a spherical electron distribution; a magnetic field applied in some direction induces a circulation of the electrons according to Lenz's law, and a field is induced which opposes the one applied. On an individual electron the induced motion confers an orbital magnetic moment which interacts with the applied field to yield a precessional motion of the moment at the Larmor frequency (equation (6)), which also represents the frequency of the electron circulation. If in a polyelectronic system the interactions between the electrons are negligible compared with their individual interactions with the applied field, all the electrons circulate

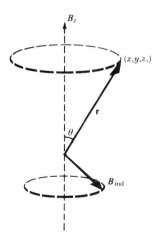

FIG. 22. In a spherical electron distribution, induced circulation of an electron produces an induced field perpendicular to its radius vector from the centre.

about the field direction at this frequency. The induced field $\mathbf{B}_{ind}$ may be calculated from Biot and Savart's law of electromagnetism. If $\mathbf{v}$ and $\mathbf{r}$ are the linear velocity and position vectors of a single electron, $\mathbf{B}_{ind} = \mu_0 e(\mathbf{v} \wedge \mathbf{r})/4\pi r^3$; we may write $\mathbf{v} = \mathbf{r} \wedge \boldsymbol{\omega}$ and substitute from equation (6). In the atom the electron has a probability $\rho(r)\,\mathrm{d}\tau$ of being a distance r from the nucleus in a volume element $\mathrm{d}\tau$: we integrate the equation over the probability distribution,

$$\mathbf{B}_{ind} = -\frac{\mu_0 e^2}{8\pi m} \int \frac{\mathbf{r} \wedge (\mathbf{B}_z \wedge \mathbf{r})}{r^3} \rho(r)\,\mathrm{d}\tau.$$

Evaluating the products,

$$\mathbf{B}_{ind} = -\frac{\mu_0 e^2 \mathbf{B}_z}{8\pi m} \int \frac{\sin\theta \rho(r)}{r}\,\mathrm{d}\tau.$$

This field is perpendicular to the distance vector, but its precession about the applied field makes its measurable component $B_{ind}\sin\theta$ (Fig. 22), which contains a term in $\sin^2\theta \ (=(x^2+y^2)/r^2)$. Since the atom is spherical,

$$\int \frac{x^2}{r^3}\rho(r)\,\mathrm{d}\tau = \int \frac{y^2}{r^3}\rho(r)\,\mathrm{d}\tau = \int \frac{z^2}{r^3}\rho(r)\,\mathrm{d}\tau$$

$$= \frac{1}{3}\int \frac{(x^2+y^2+z^2)}{r^3}\rho(r)\,\mathrm{d}\tau = \frac{1}{3}\int \frac{\rho(r)\,\mathrm{d}\tau}{r}.$$

Hence in the field direction

$$B_{ind} = -\sigma B_z = -\frac{\mu_0 e^2 B_z}{8\pi m} \cdot \frac{2}{3}\int \frac{\rho(r)}{r}\,\mathrm{d}\tau.$$

But $\mathrm{d}\tau = 4\pi r^2\,\mathrm{d}r$ and

$$\sigma = \frac{\mu_0 e^2}{3m} \int_0^\infty r\rho(r)\,\mathrm{d}\tau. \tag{22}$$

This, the Lamb equation, is easily evaluated from the wave function of the atom: for hydrogen $\rho(r) = \psi_{1s}(r)\cdot\psi_{1s}^*(r)$, and $\sigma = 17{\cdot}8 \times 10^{-6}$, $17{\cdot}8$ p.p.m. Other atoms contain larger numbers of electrons and show larger diamagnetic screening.

Molecules

Molecules normally lack the spherical symmetry of atoms and in a field the electrons may be constrained by localization in specific atoms or bonds from undergoing free circulation. The resultant diamagnetic screening is less than in an atom containing a similar number of electrons. We think of a paramagnetic contribution to the screening constant $\sigma^p \ (\leqslant 0)$, which opposes the diamagnetic term σ^d ($\geqslant 0$): $\sigma = \sigma^d + \sigma^p$. The calculation of the screening constant is complex and considers the interaction with the nucleus of the fields induced both by the applied field and by the magnetic moment of the nucleus itself. Once more perturbation theory is employed and yields

$$\sigma^d = (e^2\mu_0/12\pi m)(\overline{1/r}),$$

and

$$\sigma^p = -(e^2\mu_0/12\pi m^2)\sum_n \langle\psi_0|\hat{\mathbf{l}}|\psi_n\rangle \cdot \langle\psi_n|r^{-3}\hat{\mathbf{l}}|\psi_0\rangle/E_n - E_0.$$

The sum of the two is Ramsey's equation. The second term is similar in form to equation (21). It too must be summed over all excited states.

By the same arguments used for g-values, σ can be shown to be anisotropic. Application of a field in the z-direction of a p_z-orbital fixed in space fails to induce any resultant paramagnetic electron circulation about this axis and σ^p_{zz} is unchanged. In the orthogonal directions net circulation does occur and affects both the σ^d and σ^p values. The screening constant is also a tensor with nine components (the physical reason is obvious, see footnote, p. 38). In solution the molecule tumbles freely and an average is observed, $\sigma = \frac{1}{3}(\sigma_{xx} + \sigma_{yy} + \sigma_{zz})$. The individual components can be measured directly for certain heavy nuclei in molecules oriented in solids; for lighter nuclei the anisotropies are often too small to be measured in solids but sometimes can be obtained from studies of partially-oriented molecules (Chapter 7).

Big molecules: a compromise

Since neither the wave functions nor the excitation energies of large molecules are known, calculation of screening constants, although of fundamental interest, is not of great use. A more pragmatic approach is adopted in which contributions to the screening constant of a given nucleus from specific atoms, groups, or bonds in the molecule, and even in the solvent surrounding it, are recognized. The chemical shift is incapable of detailed calculation but this approximate approach elucidates important effects which influence it; this yields more direct physical insight into the origins and applications of chemical shifts in chemistry than would a full calculation.

The main contributions to the screening constant

These are as follows:

The diamagnetic effect at the atom containing the magnetic nucleus

Since the diamagnetic effect depends upon the electron density the proximity of any electron donating or withdrawing group may affect it. The variations in the chemical shifts of the methyl halides quoted on p. 27 result mainly from this effect.

The paramagnetic effect at the atom

The paramagnetic contribution to the screening constant is inversely proportional to the excitation energies separating the ground and excited states. In hydrogen the 1s- and 2p-orbitals are well separated and the paramagnetic contribution is relatively unimportant, even though the total spread of chemical shifts for protons is small. Other nuclei show much larger shifts and their diamagnetic contributions can be calculated quite accurately from the Lamb equation which requires only ground-state wave functions; they are invariably too small to account for the observed shifts. In ^{19}F, for example, the calculated change in σ^d between F_2 and F^-, which is spherical and has no paramagnetic screening, is 23 p.p.m., whereas the observed shift between F_2 and partially ionic HF is 625 p.p.m. The chemical shifts of ^{19}F encompass 1000 p.p.m., of ^{13}C 450 p.p.m., and of ^{31}P 700 p.p.m.; all are dominated by the paramagnetic contribution, large because of the nearness in energy of the ground and lowest states.

The effects discussed below affect the chemical shifts of ^{13}C, ^{19}F, and ^{31}P comparatively little although they are still chemically significant; for hydrogen they have major importance.

The effect of neighbouring groups

The diamagnetic and paramagnetic effects confer upon each atom a magnetic moment which in turn produces a magnetic field experienced by other nuclei. Such moments are induced also in bonds or groups of atoms; their effect is calculated quite straightforwardly for a molecule oriented in space. Imagine an individual group to have a magnetic susceptibility which, for a cylindrically symmetric system, has components $\chi_\parallel$ along the symmetry axis which we make collinear with the applied field and $\chi_\perp$ in the orthogonal directions. The magnetic susceptibility is the proportionality constant between the magnetic moment and the strength of the field which induces it: $\mu_z = B_z \chi_\parallel / \mu_0$; μ_z opposes the applied field. The magnetic field due to this magnetic moment at a nucleus a distance r away from the centre of the group can be calculated from equation (16). Since the system has cylindrical symmetry we take the nucleus to lie in the xz plane (Fig. 23). The field at the nucleus is $B_z \chi_\parallel (3\cos^2\theta - 1)/4\pi r^3 = -\Delta\sigma_{zz} B_z$, by definition, where $\Delta\sigma_{zz}$ is the incremental screening constant due to this effect. Hence $\Delta\sigma_{zz} = \chi_\parallel (1 - 3\cos^2\theta)/4\pi r^3$; similarly, for a field applied in the x- and y-directions in turn $\Delta\sigma_{xx} = \chi_\perp (1 - 3\sin^2\theta)/4\pi r^3$ and $\Delta\sigma_{yy} \doteq \chi_\perp/4\pi r^3$. In solution molecular tumbling yields an average $\Delta\sigma = (\chi_\parallel - \chi_\perp)(1 - 3\cos^2\theta)/12\pi r^3$.

This contribution to the screening constant and the chemical shift is non-zero only if the neighbouring bond or group is magnetically anisotropic. The resulting shift is either to high or to low field, depending on the signs of the susceptibility anisotropy and of the $(1 - 3\cos^2\theta)$ term, which changes on either side of $\theta = 54° 44'$. There exist therefore regions of space enclosed by

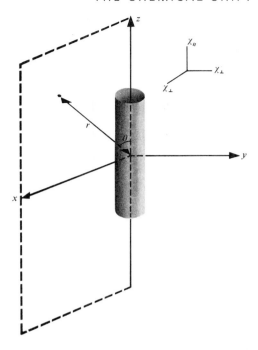

FIG. 23. For a group with a cylindrically-symmetric magnetic susceptibility tensor χ, a general point may be defined to lie in the xz-plane.

a double cone of half-angle 54° 44′ in which the resonance of a nucleus which happens to lie in these regions is shifted in one direction, whereas outside the cone the shift is in the opposite direction. Stereochemical information about the molecule in the neighbourhood of the anisotropic group can thus be deduced.

Of the common aliphatic groups, $C{=}C$ and $C{=}O$ have positive susceptibility anisotropies and their effect is depicted in Fig. 24; inside the two cones the contribution to σ is negative and the resonance shifts to low field (equation (17)). For $C{\equiv}C$ the anisotropy is of opposite sign and the effect is reversed. Its operation is apparent in the gas phase resonances of acetylene, ethylene, and ethane; if the shifts were due to diamagnetic effects, acetylene would occur at lowest field and ethane at highest. Actually the acetylene resonance lies between the other two, close to the ethane resonance. Small shifts of this type can be associated even with $C{-}C$ and $C{-}H$ bonds.

The neighbour-anisotropy effect falls off rapidly with distance and is observed only in the shifts of nuclei close to the anisotropic group in the

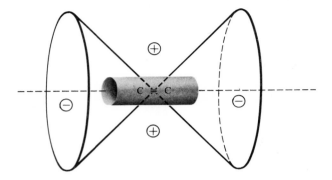

FIG. 24. The double cone surrounding the cylindrical group C=C which defines the sense of its contribution to the screening constant; a negative value implies a shift to high field of a nucleus which happens to experience the effect.

molecule. For example, both cyclohexane and cyclohexanone exist in the chair conformation in solution (with rapid interconversion between conformers); the cyclohexane resonance is at $1·44\delta$; in cyclohexanone the resonances of the methylene protons β and γ to the carbonyl group are at $1·87\delta$, but

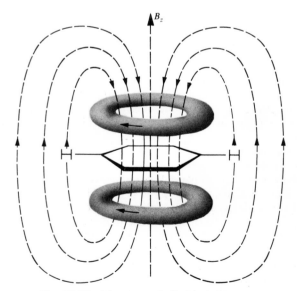

FIG. 25. The 'ring-current' effect in benzene.

the α one is at $2\cdot25\delta$. In the spectrum of diethyl ketone the methyl groups are observed at $1\cdot04$ and the methylene ones at $2\cdot39\delta$. In both examples the α-protons fall in the low-field shift region, but there is an appreciable diamagnetic effect as well.

An interesting example is found in the vicinity of a benzene ring; for this both $\chi_{\parallel}$ and $\chi_{\perp}$ are negative (where $\chi_{\parallel}$ is the component parallel to the sixfold axis) but $|\chi_{\perp}| > |\chi_{\parallel}|$ and $(\chi_{\parallel} - \chi_{\perp}) > 0$. The contributions to σ correspond to those of Fig. 24 with the cylinder axis replaced by the sixfold axis. They are exactly as expected from a simple model in which the applied field induces electron circulation in the delocalized π-orbitals when it is applied perpendicularly to the plane of the ring (Fig. 25): the shifts observed in nearby nuclei are termed *ring current shifts*. At the hydrogen atoms on the benzene ring the induced field reinforces the applied field and their resonances are shifted to low field; above and below the plane of the ring a high-field shift is predicted. This is verified by the experiment shown in Fig. 26: if chloroform is dissolved in carbon tetrachloride its resonance is progressively shifted to higher and higher

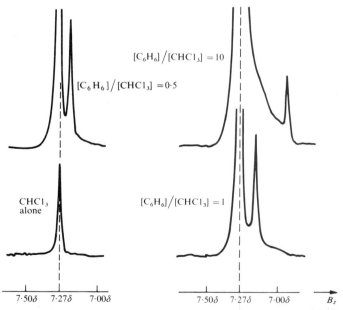

Fig. 26. The effect of adding benzene to a solution of chloroform in carbon tetrachloride is to cause the chloroform resonance to shift to high field. Although not shown in the diagram, care was taken to superimpose the T.M.S. reference line in each trace. The growing peak at low field is due to the added benzene.

field as more benzene is added; a loose complex is formed in solution in which the axis of the chloroform molecule is collinear with the sixfold axis of benzene. The magnitude of the effect can be calculated quite accurately and may be large: 0·2 nm above the plane of the ring on its axis a proton experiences a 5 p.p.m. shift to high field. It is used frequently to deduce the stereochemistries and conformations of molecules in solution. Thus the structure of the enzyme lysozyme, of molecular weight 15 000, contains twenty-one different amino acids in its primary sequence, three of which (phenylalanine, tryptophan, and tyrosine) contain phenyl residues which cause ring current shifts. Lysozyme, a large molecule, has a complex n.m.r. spectrum, much of which is still un-interpreted; above 368 K it exists in a random-coil form and the high-field part of its spectrum (Fig. 27(a)) contains a large peak originating in 128 protons from the valine, leucine, and isoleucine residues. At lower temperatures lysozyme adopts its native, tertiary, structure and has a spectrum (Fig. 27(b)) in which 48 protons are shifted to high field, many by different amounts. These shifts are due to ring-current effects from the phenyl-containing residues. The crystal structure of this enzyme is known and the ring-current shifts expected for the different protons can be calculated; the observed shifts are

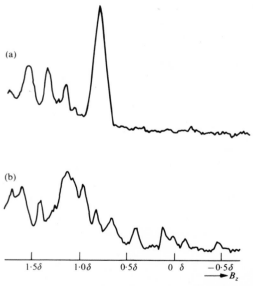

FIG. 27. The high-field region of the 220 MHz n.m.r. spectrum of lysozyme in 10 per cent solution in heavy water at pD 5·5, (a) in the random-coil form and (b) in the native tertiary structure. Ring-current shifts cause many of the resonances to shift to high field in the lower spectrum.

rationalized completely. The important conclusion is that the tertiary structure of the enzyme is the same in solution as in the crystal.

Hydrogen-bond formation

If a part of a molecule experiences a specific interaction with another part of the same molecule or with a solvent molecule its chemical shift is changed. An intra- or inter-molecular hydrogen bond may cause larger shifts than any other effect, although the mechanism is not fully understood. The shift originates most likely in a variation in the diamagnetic contribution due to a perturbed electron density or in an increased paramagnetic contribution due to the electron distribution being disturbed. The hydroxyl proton resonance in methanol varies in position by about 10 p.p.m. between the isolated molecule in dilute solution in carbon tetrachloride, where it occurs at high field, and the undiluted liquid, where it is at low field. At intermediate concentrations separate resonances from the hydrogen-bonded and non-bonded forms, which are in equilibrium, might be expected but the molecule exchanges rapidly between the two situations and a single sharp resonance is observed at an average position. For this to happen the rate of exchange should be much greater than the chemical shift, in frequency units, between protons in the two situations: in the time-scale of the experiment only the average environment of the proton is important. Exchange is observed in OH, NH, and NH_2 protons in aqueous solution (or in damp solvents) and their shifts vary with the equilibrium position. At intermediate rates of exchange a line-broadening effect occurs and their resonances may become too broad to be observed. These resonances are consequently of little use in diagnostic work of structure determination. The rate of exchange may be increased to yield sharp lines by adding small amounts of acid or alkali and n.m.r. is useful in studying such processes.

When hydrogen-bonding occurs, the resonance of the proton concerned is shifted to low field. Intramolecular bonds produce the largest effects: in salicylaldehyde resonance occurs at $11 \cdot 0\delta$ and the enolic resonance in acetyl acetone is at $15 \cdot 4\delta$.

Solvent shifts

The solvent is not usually a passive part of the system but experiences the effects discussed above which may, in benzene for example, confer a magnetic moment on the solvent molecule, the field of which is experienced by nuclei in the solute. A polar solvent affects the resonances of a polar solute in a different, electrostatic, way. The solute polarizes the solvent so that the more negative parts of the solvent molecules are attracted to its more positive end. An electric field (the 'reaction field') is set up which perturbs the electron distribution in the molecule and affects both the diamagnetic and paramagnetic contributions to the screening constants of the nuclei. (A similar effect occurs intramolecularly if a molecule contains a group with a strong electric dipole moment; the maximum effect is about 0·8 p.p.m. for hydrogen.) A chemical shift measured with reference to an internal reference compound such as T.M.S. represents the difference between the resonance positions of the protons in the solute and T.M.S. in the same solvent. It is characteristic of the solute only if T.M.S. does not interact with the solvent. (This is why T.M.S., which is inert and effectively spherical, is used as a reference compound.)

Shifts caused by diluting a given solution or by changing a solvent may out-weigh most of the effects we have discussed. Chemical shifts should be

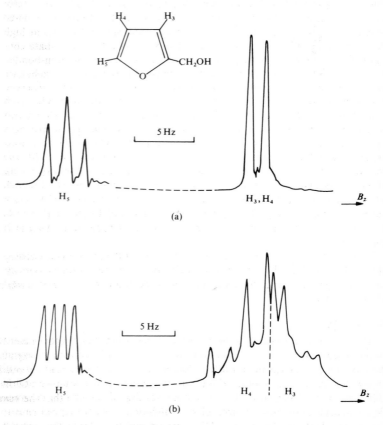

Fig. 28. The 60 MHz n.m.r. spectrum of the ring protons of 2-furfurol in solution (a) 25 per cent in benzene and (b) 50 per cent in dioxan. The latter shows strong dis-tortions of the first-order quartet patterns of two of the nuclei.

measured by extrapolating them to infinite dilution in inert solvents, a practice which, although no longer common, is essential if physical conclusions are drawn from the observed values.

The appearance of a spectrum depends upon the ratios of the chemical shifts and the coupling constants (Chapter 2) and solvent shifts may be used to vary it; the spectrum of a molecule may be too complex to decipher in one solvent but easily interpretable in another. A related effect is shown in Fig. 28, which shows the spectrum of 2-furfurol in two different solvents; in the benzene solution (above) the doublet and triplet spectrum is 'deceptively simple' since this pattern is expected from a single proton coupling equally to two equivalent ones. The 'simplicity' results from the coincidence that two protons happen to have equal chemical shifts but in the other solution this equality is removed and the expected three quartets due to each proton coupling unequally to the other two are observed. The shifts, but not the coupling constants, change between the two solutions. The lower spectrum provides an example of the intensity perturbations (described in Chapter 2) which occur when the chemical shift between two nuclei is similar to their coupling constant.

Temperature effects

The intermolecular interactions discussed in the previous section are sensitive to temperature and the shifts caused are temperature-dependent. Temperature can effect shifts in other ways. For example, rotation about a bond may be inhibited at low temperature and possible at high temperature and may lead to changes in chemical shift. In NN-dimethylnitrosamine,

$$CH_3\diagdown \qquad \diagup O$$
$$N-N \diagup$$
$$CH_3\diagup$$

at room temperature the methyl groups show two separate resonances due to the different influence of the anisotropic $N=O$ group at the *cis* and *trans* positions; as the temperature is raised rotation about the $N-N$ bond becomes more probable and the lines first broaden and then move together and finally coalesce, the width of the coalesced line decreasing as the temperature is raised further (Fig. 29). At the coalescence temperature (about 450 K) the rate of rotation is just sufficient for the methyl protons to experience a local field which is the average of those in the two separate sites: it equals the original chemical shift difference expressed in frequency units. The activation energy of the process can be calculated from the Arrhenius equation, $k = F \exp(-E/RT)$, if the frequency factor (F) is known. The coalescence temperature is difficult to define accurately, for the lines are broad, and it is better to calculate the line-shape at any temperature in terms of the exchange

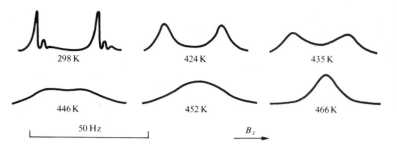

FIG. 29. The 40 MHz n.m.r. spectrum of NN-dimethyl nitrosamine at various temperatures, showing the effect of hindered rotation about the central bond.

rate, assuming initial Lorentzian shapes for the non-exchanging resonances. This treatment yields the rate of rotation at any temperature and hence both the activation energy and the frequency factor. The example chosen has an exceptionally high activation energy for rotation about a bond: 96 kJ mol^{-1}; about the C—N bond in NN-dimethylformamide it is 29·3 kJ mol^{-1}.

Another example where rapid exchange of a proton between two non-equivalent sites causes it to experience an averaged environment is in cyclohexane where rapid interconversion of the degenerate chair conformers yields a single sharp resonance; this splits into two, due to the equatorial and axial protons, at about 195 K in a 14·1 kG applied field. The chemical exchange effects discussed in the hydrogen-bonding section are further examples of two-site exchange and are amenable to the same theoretical analysis.

Similar effects occur in e.s.r. but it is unusual to observe an electron jumping between two environments in which its g-value differs. More often a rate process causes the electron to experience different hyperfine couplings at two sites and exchange causes these to be averaged. Thus the vinyl radical undergoes exchange between the two forms,

$$\underset{H}{\overset{H}{\diagdown}}C=C\overset{\bullet}{\underset{H}{\diagup}}\qquad \text{and} \qquad \underset{H}{\overset{H}{\diagdown}}C=C\overset{\diagup H}{\underset{\bullet}{\diagdown}}\quad,$$

with $A_\alpha = 44$ MHz, $A_{trans} = 192$ MHz, and $A_{cis} = 96$ MHz. At very low temperatures the spectrum consists of eight lines, as expected; at about 100 K the inner four lines broaden due to modulation of the cis and $trans$ couplings as the radical interconverts and are undetectable, but at higher temperatures they coalesce and collapse and the overall pattern is a doublet of triplets, the doublet splitting being 44 MHz and the triplet splitting 144 MHz ($= \frac{1}{2}(192 + 96)$). Modulation of hyperfine couplings leading to line-broadening occurs also in ion-pairs, by atom exchange between pairs in the naphthalene negative ion–sodium system (the hyperfine coupling from the sodium nucleus is modulated), and in electron exchange between a radical ion and its parent molecule, also in naphthalene.

Loss of spin–spin splittings in n.m.r. spectra due to exchange is common also: dry methanol shows a quartet resonance from the hydroxyl proton and a doublet from the methyl ones, whereas in normal methanol each resonance is collapsed into a single line.

Chemical shifts in paramagnetic molecules

It is a common misconception that paramagnetic molecules do not show n.m.r. spectra because rapid relaxation caused by the unpaired electrons yields lines too broad to be observed. Provided that either the electron spin relaxation rate $1/T_1 \gg A$ or its exchange rate $1/T_e \gg A$ or both, where A is the hyperfine coupling constant, the lines can be observed although they are broad compared with normal ones. An unpaired electron may produce extremely large chemical shifts by one of two effects: either by coupling of the electron and nuclear spin angular momenta through interactions communicated via the bonds (the *contact shift*; this, the mechanism of hyperfine coupling, is discussed in Chapter 5), or simply by an effect where the electron produces a 'through space' dipolar field at the nucleus (the *pseudo-contact*

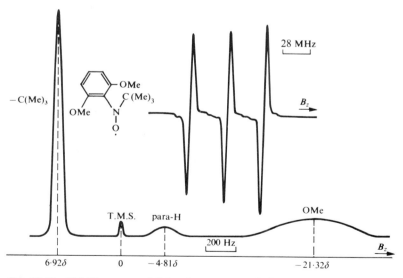

FIG. 30. The 60 MHz n.m.r. and X-band e.s.r. spectra of t-butyl-2,4-dimethoxyphenyl nitroxide. Note the size of the chemical shifts and the widths of the n.m.r. lines.

shift). Relative to the resonance position of its nearest diamagnetic analogue, R_2NOH for the radical $R_2NO\cdot$, the contact shift is $-A_I g^2 \mu_B^2 / g_I \mu_N 4kT$ p.p.m. (26·78 p.p.m./MHz at 295 K); its direction depends on the sign of A_I: if it is positive a low-field shift results, if negative a high-field one. The sign of the coupling constant cannot be obtained from normal e.s.r. spectra and n.m.r. also allows determination of coupling constants too small to be resolved in them. The n.m.r. and e.s.r. spectra of the free radical t-butyl-2,4-dimethoxy-phenyl nitroxide are shown in Fig. 30; the n.m.r. shifts are large, the line

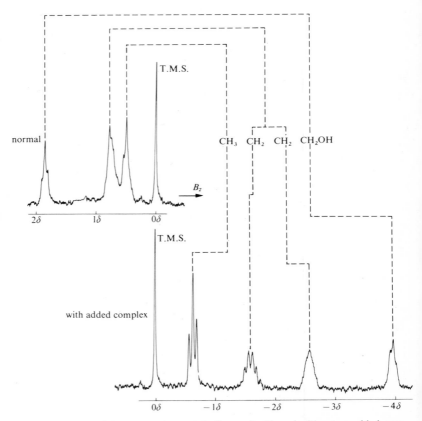

FIG. 31. The 60 MHz n.m.r. spectrum of n-butanol with and without an added para-magnetic compound, tris-(2,2,6,6-tetramethylheptan-3,5-dionato)-praseodymium, which coordinates to the oxygen atom and causes upfield shifts inversely proportional to the inverse cubes of the distances of the hydrogens from the paramagnetic centre. Europium complexes cause downfield shifts.

widths vary, and peak assignments are made on intensity considerations; the *meta* proton resonances are too broad to be observed. The e.s.r. spectrum is a triplet due to coupling between the electron and the spin-1 ^{14}N nucleus but the smaller couplings to the protons are not resolved; analysis of the n.m.r. spectrum gives A (t-butyl) = $+0.22$ MHz, A (p-hydrogen) = -0.44 MHz, A (OMe) = -0.94 MHz.

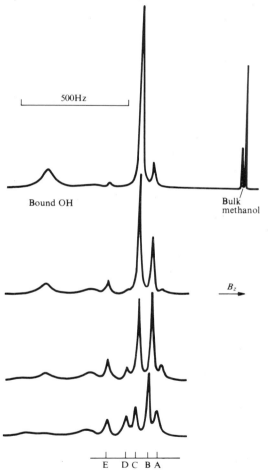

FIG. 32. The 60 MHz n.m.r. spectra of methanol solutions containing 0·25 M $Co(ClO_4)_2$ and various amounts of water at 213 K: from top to bottom the solutions are almost anhydrous, and then contain 0·348, 1·17, and 3·32 mol of water per kg of methanol.

The pseudo-contact interaction is non-zero only if the g-value of the radical is anisotropic; relative to the diamagnetic analogue it causes shifts of $-\mu_0\mu_B^2 S(S+1)(3\cos^2\theta - 1) \cdot g \cdot (g_{\parallel} - g_{\perp})/108\pi r^3 kT$ p.p.m., where S is the total spin quantum number. It is significant that the shift depends upon the inverse cube of the distance of the paramagnetic centre from the nucleus: the resonances of different nuclei in a molecule are shifted to different extents. This phenomenon is currently used to determine the absolute conformations of molecules in solution by coordinating onto them, for example at oxygen atoms, a paramagnetic ion such as Eu (III); it promises to be of great use in biological studies. These experiments, which have comparable accuracy to X-ray determinations, are unique in yielding the structures of molecules in normal solution.

Recently, paramagnetic ions have been added to solutions to cause shifts and facilitate interpretation of spectra: the ion increases the chemical shift to coupling constant ratio and simplifies the spectrum. Figure 31 shows the 60 MHz spectrum of n-butanol with and without added tris-(2,2,6,6-tetramethylheptan-3,5-dionato)-praseodymium; in the presence of the paramagnetic material the resonance of each group of equivalent protons is resolved and the spectrum is first order, although some peak-broadening occurs; in its absence the spectrum is largely indecipherable.

In Fig. 32 are shown the spectra at 213 K of methanol solutions of paramagnetic $Co(ClO_4)_2$, which contain various amounts of water: the anhydrous solution shows individual resonances from methanol in solution and in the solvation sphere of the ion (the exchange between the sites is slow). As water is added resonances from the methyl groups of the ions

$$[Co(CH_3OH)_{6-n}(H_2O)_n]^{2+}$$

are observed also: peak C originates in the

$$[Co(CH_3OH)_6]^{2+}$$

complex, peaks A and D in the diaquo complex and B and E in the mono-aquo complex. The introduction of a single water molecule into the latter causes the four equatorial methanol ligands to be inequivalent to the axial ligand in the octahedral complex.

5. Interactions between Magnetic Particles

The origins

BOTH e.s.r. and n.m.r. solution spectra display structure which originates in interactions between magnetic particles. The mechanism appears to be obvious, for electrons and nuclei are magnetic and should interact through space, as do two bar magnets. Each particle produces a dipolar field at the other (equation (16)) and, since in an applied field quantum magnets have two equal but opposite magnetic projections, two different fields result and lead to a doublet spectrum. Because of the motion of the particles we must average equation (16) over the possible values of r and θ. First consider the interaction of a proton and an electron in the spherical $1s$ orbital of the hydrogen atom: all values of θ are possible and since $\overline{\cos^2\theta} = \frac{1}{3}$ the dipolar interaction averages to zero and *cannot* cause splittings in the spectrum. If the electron occupies a higher orbital the interaction within the orbital is non-zero, but in solution molecular tumbling about the field direction causes the overall dipolar field to average to zero again; in solids a contribution to the observed splitting is obtained and is called the *anisotropic hyperfine coupling*. Similarly, the dipolar interaction between two nuclei in solution is zero on average although both in e.s.r. and n.m.r. instantaneous dipolar interactions constitute relaxation mechanisms (Chapter 1). In solids two electrons in a triplet-state radical have a non-zero interaction, the origin of fine (not hyperfine) structure in e.s.r. spectra, as do two nuclei in a molecule. These effects are discussed in Chapter 7.

In solution the origin of the splittings is the same as the hyperfine structure observed in some atomic spectra. To recognize it we re-examine the dipolar model. We assumed that within the distances encountered in an atom electrons and nuclei behave as point magnetic dipoles. In s-orbitals, however, the electron has a non-zero probability, $\psi_{1s}^2(0)$, of being at the nucleus itself and in this situation the dipole approximation fails. Without any physical model of the electron or nucleus we cannot expect to describe the resulting interaction precisely. We could consider the nucleus as a sphere of finite volume and assume that outside it the magnetic field is given by the dipole approximation. Inside, however, a magnetic polarization, given by the ratio of the nuclear magnetic moment to the volume, produces a magnetic field whose interaction energy with the electron consequently depends on the product of the magnetic moments of electron and nucleus. The magnitude of this 'Fermi contact' interaction is calculated to be

$$-(2\mu_0/3)\gamma_s\gamma_I|\psi(0)|^2\mathbf{s}\cdot\mathbf{I}$$

and the hyperfine coupling constant

$$A = -(\mu_0 h/6\pi^2)\gamma_s\gamma_I|\psi(0)|^2.$$

It is a scalar.

If the nucleus concerned is a proton, with a positive magnetogyric ratio, the negative magnetogyric ratio of the electron implies that the energy of the contact interaction is a minimum when the resolved components of the magnetic moments are parallel, that is, when the spin angular momentum projections are antiparallel. With electron and nuclear spin projections represented ↑ and ↟ respectively in a field applied parallel to the long side of the page, we represent the lowest energy configuration as ↓↟. This is only one of four possible spin combinations: the configuration ↓↡ represents a state of slightly higher energy, separated from the ground state by the hyperfine interaction energy, while ↑↟ and ↑↡ are higher states separated from ↓↟ and ↓↡ respectively by twice the energy of the electron in the applied field (equation (9)). Suppose it possible to observe the spectrum of a single atom of hydrogen in its absolute ground state: only one e.s.r. transition can occur, ↓↟ ~ ↑↟. The doublet spectrum of a bulk sample of atoms (Fig. 11(a)) reflects the ensemble nature of spectroscopy; different lines originate in different molecules at any one time. The second transition arises from the state ↓↡ : ↓↡ ~ ↑↡; the equality of the line intensities in the spectrum results from the lower two states being essentially equally populated at room temperature.

Spin–spin coupling between nuclei also originates in the Fermi contact interaction but the effect is transmitted from one nucleus to the other via the intervening bonds. Consider the hydrogen molecule, in which spin–spin coupling occurs although its effect is not observed in its spectrum because the chemical shift between the protons is zero (see Chapter 6). At each nucleus the contact interaction decrees that the electron and nuclear spins be antiparallel in the lowest energy state; the electron spins have to be antiparallel to form a bond and consequently the spin of one nucleus determines the lowest energy state of the other; the lowest energy configuration is {↓↟ : ↓↟}. We define the sign of the coupling constant to be positive if the nuclear spins are antiparallel in the lowest energy state of the molecule. If tritium, which is a spin-$\frac{1}{2}$ nucleus, is substituted into the molecule we may observe the effect of spin coupling because it has a large chemical shift from hydrogen: a bulk sample of HT yields a doublet in the hydrogen region of the spectrum and another, of equal separation, in the tritium region. Once again this implies the participation of a state above the ground state; for the hydrogen molecule this may be represented {↟↑ : ↓↟}. This state has a room-temperature population equal to that of the ground state, the difference in energy being much less than the Boltzmann (thermal) energy. It is a simple matter for the reader to construct the other two spin configurations of the molecule in the higher nuclear states.

Spin–spin interactions are very small compared with the electronic energy of the molecule and can be calculated from the second-order perturbation theory expression for the change in energy of the ground state they produce:

$$- \sum_{n \neq 0} \langle \psi_0 | \hat{H} | \psi_n \rangle \langle \psi_n | \hat{H} | \psi_0 \rangle / (E_n - E_0).$$

The operator $\hat{H}$ represents the contact interaction between each nucleus and each electron:

$$\hat{H} = (4\pi^2/h) \left(\sum_i A_{1i} \hat{s}_i \cdot \mathbf{I}_1 + \sum_i A_{2i} \hat{s}_i \cdot \mathbf{I}_2 \right).$$

where 1 and 2 are nuclei and i is an electron. Evaluating the energy, we take the term in the product $\mathbf{I}_1 \cdot \mathbf{I}_2$ and equate its coefficient to $4\pi^2 J_{12}/h$. J_{12} is a tensor and in solution its average is observed:

$$J_{12} = -\left(\frac{2}{3h} \right) (2\mu_0/3)^2 g^2 \mu_B^2 \gamma_I(1) \gamma_I(2) \sum_n \left\langle \psi_0 \left| \sum_i \hat{s}_i \delta(\mathbf{r}_{1i}) \right| \psi_n \right\rangle$$

$$\times \left\langle \psi_n \left| \sum_i \hat{s}_i \delta(\mathbf{r}_{2i}) \right| \psi_0 \right\rangle \bigg/ (E_n - E_0),$$

where r_{1i} is the distance between electron i and nucleus 1 and $\delta(\mathbf{r}_{1i})$ is a delta function which picks out the value of the function when the electron is at the nucleus. The expression must be summed over all excited states (actually only the triplet ones in this case, due to the properties of spin operators).

The contact interaction is one of three possible interactions between the spins of two nuclei. A second originates in each nucleus inducing circulation of electrons to produce fields experienced by the other and the third in a dipolar interaction between electron and nucleus. If the nuclear environment is not spherically symmetric one of the electron spin states is of lower energy than the other, resulting in more electrons in one state than the other and a non-zero magnetic field due to the electron at the other nucleus. For ^{1}H these two mechanisms contribute negligibly to the coupling constant and for all nuclei the contact term is dominant. Whatever the mechanism, the coupling constant is directly proportional to the product of the magnetogyric ratios of the nuclei which couple. This allows the determination of coupling constants between nuclei of similar chemical shift by isotopic substitution; introduction of a deuterium atom, which has an enormous chemical shift from hydrogen, into methane allows J_{HH} to be obtained from the observed value of J_{HD} and the relation $J_{HH}/J_{HD} = \gamma_H/\gamma_D = 6.515$; its magnitude is 12·4 Hz (and is actually negative).

For comparison of couplings between different nuclei a 'reduced' coupling constant is defined: $K_{ij} = (J_{ij}/h)(2\pi/\gamma_i)(2\pi/\gamma_j)$. Its advantage is seen when couplings expected to be similar for chemical reasons are compared: the

^{13}C—H directly-bonded coupling has J and K both positive; the ^{29}Si—H coupling has a negative J, since γ_{Si} is negative, but a positive K ($K_{CH} = 4\cdot1 \times 10^{-20}$N A^2 m^{-3}; $K_{SiH} = 8\cdot5 \times 10^{-20}$N A^2 m^{-3}).

Hyperfine interactions

Hyperfine splitting is observed only from species whose unpaired electron occupies an orbital of some s-character centred on a magnetic nucleus. The orbital may have partial s-character, for example 25 per cent in sp^3, or resultant unpaired spin density may be induced in an s-orbital which normal bonding theory would suggest contained two paired electrons.

Radical geometry

If an electron occupies an sp^n-orbital in a radical, its wave function is written (equation (22))

$$\Psi = c_s\psi_s + c_p\psi_p + \ldots + c_i\psi_i + \ldots,$$

where atomic orbitals ψ_i are localized on different atoms. With normalized wave functions, $\langle\psi_i|\psi_i\rangle = 1$, and if overlap between orbitals is neglected, $\langle\psi_i|\psi_j\rangle = 0$ and

$$\langle\Psi|\Psi\rangle = 1 = c_s^2\langle\psi_s|\psi_s\rangle + c_p^2\langle\psi_p|\psi_p\rangle + \ldots + c_i^2\langle\psi_i|\psi_i\rangle$$
$$+ \ldots = c_s^2 + c_p^2 + \ldots + c_i^2 + \ldots.$$

Hence the coefficients c_s^2 and c_p^2 represent the probabilities that the electron occupies the s- and p-orbitals respectively. A measurement performed on an isolated atom with the electron in a pure s-orbital would yield a coupling constant A_s^0, corresponding to $c_s^2 = 1$, but this value usually must be calculated. In molecular orbital theory it is assumed that the wave function is unchanged from the isolated atom and if a coupling A_s is observed, $c_s^2 = A_s/A_s^0$. Similarly, if the anisotropic hyperfine coupling to a p-electron is observed in a solid, $c_p^2 = A_p/A_p^0$. The relative s- and p-characters determine the shape of sp^n-orbitals which, in turn, determine the local geometry of molecules containing them: if it is assumed that the bonds formed from the hybridization are mutually orthogonal, the bond angle may be calculated from bonding theory in terms of the ratio $(c_p/c_s)^2$; for C_{2v} and C_{3v} triatomic groups the results are shown in Fig. 33.

From the experimental observations a bond angle of 133° is obtained for NO$_2$, similar to the gas phase value of 134°, and 116° for NO$_3^{2-}$. The values obtained are susceptible to the approximations inherent in the theory.

Spin polarization

For an unpaired electron in a carbon $2s$ orbital $A_C^0 = 3330$ MHz and an sp^3-hybrid would yield one-quarter this value. Observations on ^{13}CH$_3$.

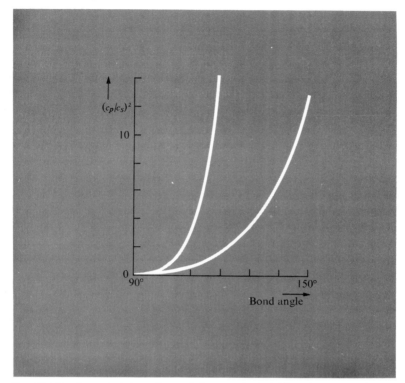

FIG. 33. The theoretical dependence of the quantity $(c_p/c_s)^2$ on bond angle for tri-atomic groups of C_{2v} and C_{3v} symmetry.

show $A_C = 107 \cdot 8$ MHz; we deduce that the atom is sp^2-hybridized with the unpaired electron in the atomic $2p$-orbital and that the radical is planar. The unpaired s-electron spin density needed at the nucleus for hyperfine coupling results from a 'spin-polarization' mechanism. With reference to the single C—H fragment (Fig. 34), the electron in the sp^2-orbital may have either the same (a) or the opposite (b) spin to the unpaired p-electron. If no electron were in the p-orbital, (a) and (b) would be equally likely but, by analogy with Hund's rule ('electrons enter equivalent orbitals with parallel spins'), in its presence (a) is of lower energy. (This conclusion is justified strictly if the exchange forces between the electrons are calculated.) Because the sp^2-hybrid has one-third s-character the presence of unequal amounts of the two spin states gives rise to unpaired spin density at the nucleus. The proton coupling in methyl (Fig. 12) arises similarly: with (a) favoured over (b),

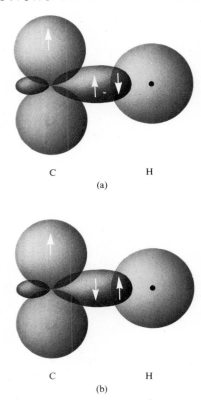

FIG. 34. The mechanism of spin polarization: electron exchange interactions cause configuration (a) to be of lower energy than (b).

the 1s hydrogen orbital has a preponderance of one spin over the other and a net unpaired s-electron density at the nucleus. The predominant spin is opposite to that of the unpaired electron; the orbital is said to have a *negative spin density* and the hyperfine coupling constant is negative. The carbon has a positive spin density and coupling constant.

Spin-polarization is the source of hyperfine coupling in aromatic radical ions in which the unpaired electron occupies a π-orbital. The spectrum of the benzene negative ion (Fig. 35) shows that the electron couples equally to each proton. Since the unpaired electron density at the proton results from an unpaired electron at the α-C atom, the hyperfine coupling constant is directly proportional to the probability of finding an electron there. This is summarized

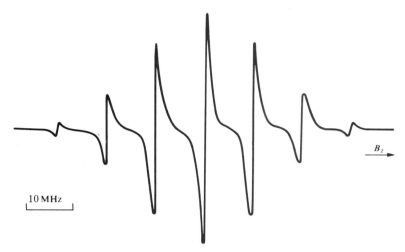

FIG. 35. The e.s.r. spectrum of the benzene anion.

in the McConnell equation

$$A_H = Q \cdot \rho_p, \tag{24}$$

where ρ_p is the electron density in the carbon p-orbital and Q is a constant. For $\cdot CH_3$, $\rho_p = 1$, $A_H = -64.5$ MHz, and $Q = -64.5$ MHz; for the benzene anion $\rho_p = \frac{1}{6}$ (by symmetry), $A_H = -10.5$ MHz, and $Q = -63$ MHz: the latter value is usually used.

In aromatic radical ions the π- and σ-electrons are largely independent (spin-polarization is negligible in determining the electronic character of molecules) and we write $\Psi_\pi = \sum_i c_i \psi_p^{(i)}$ where $c_i^2 = \rho_p^{(i)}$ and can be determined experimentally from equation (24). The accuracy of simple molecular orbital theory calculations, for example Hückel theory, can be checked experimentally: for radical anions containing even numbers of carbon atoms the agreement is excellent, as it is for symmetric heterocyclics such as the pyrazine anion for which calculation yields $\rho_C = 0.116$ and $\rho_N = 0.274$ and experiment 0.118 and 0.272. The pyrazine spectrum (Fig. 36) indicates the electron couples equally to two spin-1 ^{14}N nuclei to give a $1:2:3:2:1$ intensity ratio quintet each line of which is further split into a $1:4:6:4:1$ quintet by equal coupling to four protons. The unpaired electron occupies the lowest antibonding orbital; interestingly, theory indicates that the highest bonding orbital is delocalized only over the carbon atoms: the spectrum of the positive ion, which has not been prepared, should be a simple quintet.

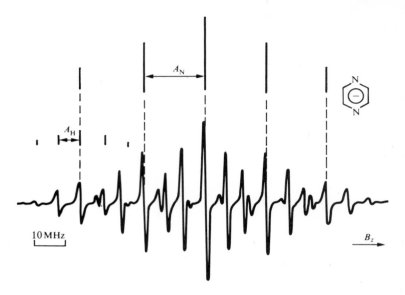

FIG. 36. The e.s.r. spectrum of the pyrazine anion showing the quintet due to coupling to two equivalent spin-1 ^{14}N nuclei further split by coupling to four equivalent protons. Only one sub-quintet is shown for clarity.

Coupling to protons attached to β-carbon atoms

In saturated radicals coupling over two bonds is greater than that over one; in ethyl, for example, $A_\alpha = 62.7$ MHz and $A_\beta = 75.2$ MHz. Spin polarization cannot account for this and its origin lies in hyperconjugation: overlap of the 2p-orbital on the α-C atom with the sp^3 hybrids on the β one leads directly to delocalization of unpaired spin density into the hydrogen orbital. With reference to Fig. 37, the overlap is greatest when the axes of the carbon orbitals are co-planar; defining a dihedral angle, θ, as the angle between the axis of the p-orbital and the projection of the β C—H bond onto the plane containing the axis, hyperconjugation is expected to vary as $\cos^2\theta$ since the electron density in a p-orbital shows this angular dependence. Experimentally $A_\beta = B_0 + B_1 \cos^2\theta$ where B_0 and B_1 are constants. If the sole coupling mechanism were hyperconjugation, coupling should be zero when $\theta = 90°$; a small residual coupling is observed and necessitates the B_0 term. For the conformationally-locked cyclobutyl radical $A_\beta = 102.8$ MHz with $\theta = 30°$; in ethyl free rotation occurs about the C—C bond and we observe an average $\overline{\cos^2\theta} = \frac{1}{2}\int_0^{2\pi}\cos^2\theta \, d\theta = \frac{1}{2}$. Hence $B_0 = 20$ MHz and $B_1 = 110.4$ MHz; they are not completely constant and care must be taken in deducing dihedral angles using them.

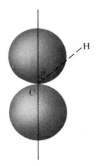

FIG. 37. The definition of the dihedral angle θ.

Spin–spin coupling

The lack of low-lying excited states in hydrogen causes its coupling behaviour to differ qualitatively from other $I = \frac{1}{2}$ nuclei but the bulk of data concerns hydrogen and we concentrate on this. Spin-coupling energies are small compared with hyperfine ones (in H_2 $J_{HH} = 280$ Hz; in H· $A_H = 1420$ MHz) and miniscule compared with orbital energies; neither the magnitudes nor the signs of coupling constants are accurately calculable although much effort has been applied to the problem. For example, the coupling mechanism described already for H_2 if applied to a CH_2 group suggests that the lowest energy state is $\{\downarrow\uparrow\downarrow\,;\,\downarrow\uparrow\downarrow\}$ (the 'central' electrons have parallel spins since they inhabit similar orbitals on carbon) and that the coupling constant is negative. Experiment shows that this coupling constant over two bonds, ^2J, has either sign and varies from $-21\cdot5$ Hz in cyclopentene-3,5-dione to $42\cdot4$ Hz in formaldehyde. The values depend upon substituents and show slight solvent and temperature dependence.

In simple hydrocarbons ^2J increases positively as the s-character of the carbon orbital increases: in methane it is $-12\cdot4$ Hz, in ethylene $2\cdot5$ Hz. An electronegative substituent on the α-C atom increases ^2J but on the β-carbon reduces it; empirically, for substituted ethylenes $CH_2 = CXY$, $^2J = [\{61\cdot6/(E_X + E_Y)\} - 12\cdot9]$ Hz, where E is the electronegativity. If the methylene group is adjacent to a π-electron distribution ^2J decreases $(-14\cdot5$ Hz in toluene) and the effect is greatest when the H—H axis is perpendicular to the nodal plane of the π-electrons, suggesting hyperconjugation. These trends in ^2J have been rationalized using molecular orbital theory.

Coupling constants over three bonds between protons attached to adjacent sp^3-hybridized carbons are 0–20 Hz and positive (as expected: $\{\downarrow\uparrow\downarrow\,;\,\downarrow\uparrow\,;\,\uparrow\downarrow\uparrow\}$). The situation is similar to an electron coupling to a proton and has a similar angle dependence. This is chemically very significant for

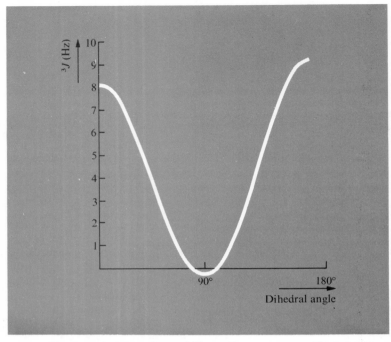

FIG. 38. The theoretical dependence of ^3J coupling constants on dihedral angle; a negative ^3J proton coupling has never been observed.

it implies that the relative configurations of adjacent carbon atoms and the stereochemistry of the molecule can be deduced from ^3J values; in six-membered saturated ring compounds the observed coupling between axial protons is 8–14 Hz but between equatorial ones, or an axial–equatorial pair, it is 1–7 Hz. Quantitatively, the Karplus equation states

$$^3J = J_0 + J_1 \cos \theta + J_2 \cos 2\theta \approx J_3 + J_4 \cos^2\theta, \qquad (25)$$

where J_{0-4} are constants and θ is the dihedral angle separating the C—H bonds. Theoretically, $J_0 = 4.2$ Hz, $J_1 = -0.5$ Hz, and $J_2 = 4.5$ Hz and the predicted angular dependence is shown in Fig. 38; however these constants cannot be calculated accurately and, moreover, ^3J values vary with substituent. They decrease if the substituent is electronegative, if the CCH bond angle increases, and if the C—C bond length increases. The second form of the equation is used often and the constants determined empirically from measurements on rigid ring compounds whose solution conformations are believed known; precise values of θ cannot be deduced from measurements

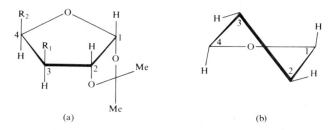

(a)   (b)

FIG. 39. (a) The structural formula of 1,2-isopropylidene-α-D-xylohexofuranose derivatives. (b) The conformation of the furanose ring in solution.

(although the contrary is sometimes claimed) and the equation should be used only in a semi-quantitative manner, for example to decide whether two protons in a saturated molecule are in *trans* or *gauche* configurations. This is sufficient to determine molecular conformations in solution. An example is found in a study of 1,2-isopropylidene-α-D-xylohexofuranose derivatives (Fig. 39(a)): thirteen showed coupling constants $^3J_{1,2} \approx 3.6$ Hz, $^3J_{2,3} < 0.5$ Hz and $^3J_{3,4} \approx 3.0$ Hz. Reference to equation (25) shows these values to be consistent only with the skew conformation of the furanose ring (Fig. 39(b)): the near equality of $^3J_{1,2}$ and $^3J_{3,4}$ implies that the ring is symmetrically deformed out of the plane and the low value of $^3J_{2,3}$ that $\theta_{2,3} \approx 90°$. The tempting possibility of using the equation to decide which substituent groups cause the greatest ring buckling from precise J values is not justified.

Three-bond couplings in ethylenic systems depend on both the stereochemistry of the molecule and the electronegativity of substituents: *trans* ^3J values, 10–18 Hz, are always greater than *cis* values, 6–14 Hz, in the same molecule. They are inversely proportional to the sum of the electronegativities of the substituents.

In phenyl rings ^3J *ortho* couplings are 7–10 Hz, ^4J *meta* couplings 2–3 Hz and ^5J *para* couplings 0–1 Hz, and again vary with electronegativity of substituents. The 'long-range' (over more than three bonds) couplings are characteristic of unsaturated compounds although the mechanism in aromatics is uncertain. In allylic (H—C=C—C—H) and homoallylic

(H—C—C=C—C—H) fragments long-range coupling is transmitted hyperconjugatively through the π-electron system and varies with the dihedral angle between the C—H bond and the nodal plane.

In organic and inorganic chemistry measurements of coupling constants aid elucidation of molecular structure and conformation, and a great many are listed in the literature. Frustratingly, their magnitudes are usually too

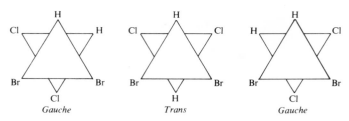

FIG. 40. The three rotational isomers of $CHCl_2CHBr_2$ shown looking along the C—C bond axis: the other atoms appear at the vertices of equilateral triangles.

small to allow physical deductions since many factors affect the values. An exception is the study of rotational isomerism about a single bond: a substituted ethane, $CHCl_2CHBr_2$, has three rotational isomers (Fig. 40), the two *gauche* isomers being equivalent. If the molecule is locked in one rotamer the coupling constant observed is either J_T (in the *trans* form) or J_G (in the others); however the enthalpy difference between rotamers, ΔH, is low, rotation occurs, and the observed average coupling

$$\bar{J} = \{p_T J_T + (1 - p_T) J_G\},$$

where p_T is the fraction of the *trans* isomer. From the Boltzmann law $p_T/(1 - p_T) = \exp(\Delta H/RT)$ and if suitable values of J_T and J_G are obtained from the literature and equation (25), ΔH may be obtained. If a disubstituted ethane, CH_2ClCH_2Br, is studied two separate average couplings are observed and it is necessary only to assume dihedral angles of the isomers and apply equation (25) to extract the enthalpy difference. Qualitatively, since $J_T > J_G$, an increase in $\bar{J}$ with temperature implies that the *gauche* isomer is the more stable, and conversely.

6. Analysis of Spectra

IN this chapter the quantum mechanics necessary to the interpretation of complex spectra is given, using the definitions listed in the Appendix. We assume that the energies of magnetic particles are independent of other properties of the molecule containing them and can be discussed separately. We calculate these energies, using the operator equation $\hat{H}\Psi = E\Psi$, and regard the B_1 field as producing transitions between the states to which the energies correspond.

The energy operator $\hat{H}$

$\hat{H}$ can be written $(\hat{H}^{(0)} + \hat{H}^{(1)})$, where $\hat{H}^{(0)}$ represents the interaction of the magnetic moment of the particle with the applied field and $\hat{H}^{(1)}$ the mutual coupling of the particles. They are obtained by replacing the angular momentum vectors of the classical equations by their corresponding operators:

$$\hat{H}^{(0)} = - \sum_i \gamma_i B_z(i) \hat{P}_z(i),$$

where $\gamma_i = \gamma_s$ if i is an electron and γ_I if a nucleus,

$$\hat{H}^{(1)} = (4\pi^2/h) \sum_{i<j} C_{ij} \hat{\mathbf{P}}(i) . \hat{\mathbf{P}}(j)$$

$$= (4\pi^2/h) \sum_{i<j} C_{ij} \{\hat{P}_x(i)\hat{P}_x(j) + \hat{P}_y(i)\hat{P}_y(j) + \hat{P}_z(i)\hat{P}_z(j)\},$$

where $C_{ij} = A_{ij}$ if either i or j is an electron and J_{ij} otherwise. We recall the convention of Chapter 1 that P denotes s or I depending on its context.

The wave functions

For spin-$\frac{1}{2}$ particles we designate the state function of the $m_p = \frac{1}{2}$ state α, and the $m_p = -\frac{1}{2}$ state, β; the electron has β as its lower state, the proton α. These states have the properties, in operator language, $\hat{P}_z\alpha = \frac{1}{2}\hbar\alpha$ and $\hat{P}_z\beta = -\frac{1}{2}\hbar\beta$. If a molecule contains more than one magnetic particle, we write the spin function as the *basic product function*:

$$\Psi = \alpha(1)\beta(2)\beta(3) \ldots \equiv \alpha\beta\beta \ldots ,$$

where it is implied that particle 1 is in the α-state, 2 in the β-state, and so on. In a radical one of these state functions refers to the electron spin.

The spectrum of a single particle

Only $\hat{H}^{(0)}$ remains when one particle is present and we wish to solve the energy equation, if the particle is in the α-state, $\hat{H}^{(0)}\alpha = E\alpha$. Multiplying each side by the complex conjugate and integrating,

$$\langle\alpha|\hat{H}^{(0)}|\alpha\rangle = E\langle\alpha|\alpha\rangle = E$$

but

$$\langle\alpha|\hat{H}^{(0)}|\alpha\rangle = -\langle\alpha|\gamma_i B_z \hat{P}_z|\alpha\rangle = -\tfrac{1}{2}\hbar\gamma_i B_z\langle\alpha|\alpha\rangle.$$

Thus the energy of the particle is $-\tfrac{1}{2}\hbar\gamma_i B_z = -\tfrac{1}{2}g_i\mu_i B_z$. To induce a transition to the β-state a varying magnetic field $B_1\cos 2\pi\nu t$ is applied at the resonance frequency ν in the x-direction and this interacts with the x-component of the angular momentum. The energy operator describing the interaction is itself time-dependent:

$$\hat{H}(t) = \gamma_i B_1\cos(2\pi\nu t)\hat{P}_x \equiv k\hat{P}_x\cos(2\pi\nu t).$$

Whether or not this produces a transition can be calculated from time-dependent perturbation theory which yields the result for the rate of transition between two states m and n:

$$W_{mn} = (k^2/h^2)|\langle\psi_m|\hat{P}_x|\psi_n\rangle|^2\delta(E_m - E_n - h\nu),$$

where the delta function picks out the value when $h\nu = E_m - E_n$. Experience shows this to be most easily evaluated by defining two new operators $\hat{P}^+ = (\hat{P}_x + i\hat{P}_y)$ and $\hat{P}^- = (\hat{P}_x - i\hat{P}_y)$. Their properties are derived in standard quantum mechanics texts: $\hat{P}^+\alpha = 0$, $\hat{P}^-\alpha = \hbar\beta$, $\hat{P}^+\beta = \hbar\alpha$, and $\hat{P}^-\beta = 0$. When $\hat{P}^+$ acts on a function its m_p value increases by one, when $\hat{P}^-$ acts, m_p decreases by one; consequently the operators are known as shift operators. We see that $\hat{P}_x = \tfrac{1}{2}(\hat{P}^+ + \hat{P}^-)$ and for a transition $\alpha\leftrightarrow\beta$,

$$W_{\alpha\beta}^{\frac{1}{2}} \propto \tfrac{1}{2}\langle\alpha|\hat{P}^+ + \hat{P}^-|\beta\rangle = \tfrac{1}{2}\langle\alpha|\hat{P}^+|\beta\rangle + \tfrac{1}{2}\langle\alpha|\hat{P}^-|\beta\rangle = \hbar/2.$$

This is non-zero and the transition is allowed; in general the overall selection rule is $\Delta m_p = \pm 1$.

The operator $\hat{H}^{(1)}$ can also be expressed conveniently in terms of shift operators:

$$\hat{H}^{(1)} = (4\pi^2/h)\sum_{i<j} C_{ij}[\hat{P}_z(i)\hat{P}_z(j) + \tfrac{1}{2}\{\hat{P}^+(i)\hat{P}^-(j) + \hat{P}^-(i)\hat{P}^+(j)\}]. \tag{26}$$

The spectrum of a molecule or radical containing two magnetic particles

Wave functions that satisfy the energy equation are called eigenstates of the system. For systems containing two magnetic particles A and B there are four basic product functions $\alpha\alpha$, $\alpha\beta$, $\beta\alpha$, and $\beta\beta$ but these are not necessarily eigenstates of the four energy levels. By normal methods of quantum mechanics, however, we can construct the four eigenstates by taking linear combinations of the basic product functions. For example, for the first eigenstate,

$$\Psi_1 = c_1\alpha\alpha + c_2\alpha\beta + c_3\beta\alpha + c_4\beta\beta. \tag{27}$$

Inserting this into the energy equation, multiplying by $(\alpha\alpha)^*$, and integrating we obtain

$$c_1\langle\alpha\alpha|\hat{H}|\alpha\alpha\rangle + c_2\langle\alpha\alpha|\hat{H}|\alpha\beta\rangle + c_3\langle\alpha\alpha|\hat{H}|\beta\alpha\rangle + c_4\langle\alpha\alpha|\hat{H}|\beta\beta\rangle$$

$$= E_1(c_1\langle\alpha\alpha|\alpha\alpha\rangle + c_2\langle\alpha\alpha|\alpha\beta\rangle + c_3\langle\alpha\alpha|\beta\alpha\rangle + c_4\langle\alpha\alpha|\beta\beta\rangle)$$

$$= E_1 c_1. \tag{28}$$

We have now to evaluate the integrals,

$$\langle\alpha\alpha|\hat{H}^{(0)}|\alpha\alpha\rangle = -\langle\alpha\alpha|\gamma_A B_z(A)\hat{P}_z(A) + \gamma_B B_z(B)\hat{P}_z(B)|\alpha\alpha\rangle$$

$$= -\{\langle\alpha\alpha|\gamma_A B_z(A)\hat{P}_z(A)|\alpha\alpha\rangle + \langle\alpha\alpha|\gamma_B B_z(B)\hat{P}_z(B)|\alpha\alpha\rangle\}$$

$$= -\tfrac{1}{2}\hbar\gamma_A B_z(A) - \tfrac{1}{2}\hbar\gamma_B B_z(B) \equiv -E_A^{(0)} - E_B^{(0)}$$

$$\langle\alpha\alpha|\hat{H}^{(1)}|\alpha\alpha\rangle = (4\pi^2 C_{AB}/h)\{\langle\alpha\alpha|\hat{P}_z(A)\hat{P}_z(B)|\alpha\alpha\rangle$$

$$+ \tfrac{1}{2}\langle\alpha\alpha|\hat{P}^+(A)\hat{P}^-(B) + \hat{P}^-(A)\hat{P}^+(B)|\alpha\alpha\rangle\}$$

$$= (4\pi^2 C_{AB}/h)(\langle\alpha|\hat{P}_z|\alpha\rangle\langle\alpha|\hat{P}_z|\alpha\rangle + 0) = hC_{AB}/4.$$

However all other integrals are zero, for example,

$$\langle\alpha\alpha|\hat{H}^{(0)}|\alpha\beta\rangle = -\{\langle\alpha\alpha|\gamma_A B_z(A)\hat{P}_z(A)|\alpha\beta\rangle + \langle\alpha\alpha|\gamma_B B_z(B)\hat{P}_z(B)|\alpha\beta\rangle\}$$

$$= -\{\langle\alpha|\gamma_A B_z(A)\hat{P}_z(A)|\alpha\rangle\langle\alpha|\beta\rangle + \langle\alpha|\alpha\rangle\langle\alpha|\gamma_B B_z(B)\hat{P}_z(B)|\beta\rangle\}$$

$$= -\{0 - \tfrac{1}{2}\hbar\gamma_B B_z(B)\langle\alpha|\alpha\rangle\langle\alpha|\beta\rangle\} = 0.$$

The reader may verify that the others are zero too. Thus equation (28) becomes $c_1\{-E_A^{(0)} - E_B^{(0)} + hC_{AB}/4\} = E_1 c_1$, or $E_1 = -E_A^{(0)} - E_B^{(0)} + hC_{AB}/4$. The coefficient is evaluated from the normalization condition $\sum_i c_i^2 = 1 : c_1 = 1$ and in fact $\alpha\alpha$ is an eigenstate of the system and, by symmetry, the same must be true for $\beta\beta$.

The four equations such as (28) are summarized conveniently in matrix form where we number the functions $\alpha\alpha$, $\alpha\beta$, $\beta\alpha$, and $\beta\beta$ as 1 to 4 and use the short-hand notation $H_{11} = \langle\alpha\alpha|\hat{H}|\alpha\alpha\rangle$, etc:

$$\begin{bmatrix} H_{11}-E & 0 & 0 & 0 \\ 0 & H_{22}-E & H_{23} & 0 \\ 0 & H_{32} & H_{33}-E & 0 \\ 0 & 0 & 0 & H_{44}-E \end{bmatrix} \begin{bmatrix} c_1 \\ c_2 \\ c_3 \\ c_4 \end{bmatrix} = 0. \tag{29}$$

We see from this that $\alpha\beta$ and $\beta\alpha$ are not eigenstates of the system and to deduce the true wave functions and their energies we must solve the 2×2

submatrix, whose actual form with the matrix elements evaluated is

$$\begin{bmatrix} -E_A^{(0)} + E_B^{(0)} - hC_{AB}/4 - E & hC_{AB}/2 \\ hC_{AB}/2 & E_A^{(0)} - E_B^{(0)} - hC_{AB}/4 - E \end{bmatrix} \begin{bmatrix} c_2 \\ c_3 \end{bmatrix} = 0.$$

To solve the energy determinant we write $E = \frac{1}{2}$ (sum of the diagonal elements neglecting E) + $\varepsilon = -hC_{AB}/4 + \varepsilon$, where ε is to be determined; $K \cos 2\theta = \frac{1}{2}$ (difference in the diagonal elements) = $-(E_A^{(0)} - E_B^{(0)})$; $K \sin 2\theta =$ off-diagonal element = $hC_{AB}/2$. The determinant becomes

$$\begin{vmatrix} K \cos 2\theta - \varepsilon & K \sin 2\theta \\ K \sin 2\theta & -K \cos 2\theta - \varepsilon \end{vmatrix} = 0.$$

Expanding and solving gives $\varepsilon = \pm K$: the energies of the eigenstates are $(-hC_{AB}/4 \pm K)$, where $K = [\{-E_A^{(0)} + E_B^{(0)}\}^2 + h^2 C_{AB}^2/4]^{\frac{1}{2}}$. Solution for c_2 and c_3 gives $c_2/c_3 = \cos\theta/\sin\theta$ and since $c_2^2 + c_3^2 = 1$ for normalization, $c_2 = \cos\theta$ and $c_3 = \sin\theta$. The wave functions and energies of the four states are summarized in Table 3 together with their corresponding $\sum m_p$ values. We note that states with different $\sum m_p$ values do not mix, a general result which allows all off-diagonal elements connecting them to be written zero.

Transitions occur according to the rule $\Delta m_p = \pm 1$ for each particle (strictly $\Delta \sum m_p = \pm 1$ for the system); their relative intensities are easily determined, for example for the transition $1 \leftrightarrow 3$,

$$W_{12} \propto |\langle \alpha\alpha | \hat{P}_x(A) + \hat{P}_x(B) | \sin\theta(\alpha\beta) + \cos\theta(\beta\alpha) \rangle|^2$$
$$= (\hbar^2/4)(\sin\theta + \cos\theta)^2 = (\hbar^2/4)(1 + \sin 2\theta).$$

The spectra we calculate for two magnetic particles show a continuous gradation in behaviour as $(E_A^{(0)} - E_B^{(0)})$ varies from large magnitudes to the energy of the magnetic interaction hC_{AB} and eventually to zero. The former situation corresponds to the 'first-order' case and applies to the e.s.r. spectrum

TABLE 3

State	Σm_p	Wave function	Energy
1	1	$\alpha\alpha$	$-E_A^{(0)} - E_B^{(0)} + hC_{AB}/4$
2	0	$\cos\theta(\alpha\beta) - \sin\theta(\beta\alpha)$	$-hC_{AB}/4 - K$
3	0	$\sin\theta(\alpha\beta) + \cos\theta(\beta\alpha)$	$-hC_{AB}/4 + K$
4	-1	$\beta\beta$	$E_A^{(0)} + E_B^{(0)} + hC_{AB}/4$

Relative intensities of transitions

$1 \leftrightarrow 3$	$1 + \sin 2\theta$	$2 \leftrightarrow 4$	$1 - \sin 2\theta$
$1 \leftrightarrow 2$	$1 - \sin 2\theta$	$3 \leftrightarrow 4$	$1 + \sin 2\theta$

of the hydrogen atom and to the n.m.r. spectra of nuclei whose resonances are separated by a large chemical shift; the e.s.r. spectrum is simply the special case when one particle is an electron. The situation where $(E_A^{(0)} - E_B^{(0)}) \sim hC_{AB}$ is found commonly in n.m.r. spectra and the extreme case when it is zero implies that the chemical shifts of the two nuclei are the same. We consider all these situations below where it is convenient to perform the artificial separation into e.s.r. and n.m.r. cases for two reasons: first because the electron has a negative magnetogyric ratio, which causes the relative order of the states in Table 3 to differ from that of the nuclear case of two protons, and second because e.s.r. unlike n.m.r. is discussed conventionally in terms of g-factors.

The e.s.r. spectrum of hydrogen atoms

We take A as the electron, B the proton: $E_A^{(0)} = \frac{1}{2}h\gamma_s B_z = -\frac{1}{2}g_e\mu_B B_z$; $E_B^{(0)} = \frac{1}{2}g_I\mu_N B_z$; and $C_{AB} = A_H$. Since $|E_A^{(0)}| > |E_B^{(0)}|$ and is of opposite sign, the states in Table 3 fall in order of increasing energy 2, 4, 3, and 1. Only two electron transitions occur, $2 \leftrightarrow 1$ and $4 \leftrightarrow 3$ (Fig. 41) and the spectrum is a doublet of separation A_H Hz, centred at a frequency $(1/h)(\frac{1}{2}g_e\mu_B B_z - \frac{1}{2}g_I\mu_N B_z + K)$ where $K = [(\frac{1}{2}g_e\mu_B B_z + \frac{1}{2}g_I\mu_N B_z)^2 + h^2 A_H^2/4]^{\frac{1}{2}}$. The hyperfine coupling constant may be measured directly from the spectrum, a special case which occurs in n.m.r. also when only two nuclei couple. In situations which involve more

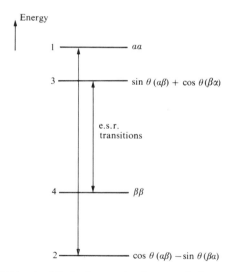

FIG. 41. The energy levels of the hydrogen atom in an applied magnetic field, showing the e.s.r. transitions.

than two coupled particles and which are not 'first-order' in nature, it is not possible in general to measure coupling constants directly from the spectrum although certain of them can be measured in particular cases. This happens, for example, if in a system of three particles A, B, and X two have values $E_A^{(0)}$ and $E_B^{(0)}$ which are almost the same whereas the third has an $E_X^{(0)}$ value which is widely different: C_{AB} can be measured directly; this is because the off-diagonal matrix elements involving X are zero and the AB region of the spectrum consists of two sub-spectra corresponding to the $m_p = \pm\frac{1}{2}$ states of the particle X.

At normal e.s.r. operating field strengths, the coupling energy is negligible compared to the energy possessed by the particles owing to their presence in the field and $K = (\frac{1}{2}g_e\mu_B B_z + \frac{1}{2}g_I\mu_N B_z)$. The spectrum consequently is centred at $(1/h)g_e\mu_B B_z$ Hz and the approximation implies that $\sin 2\theta = 0$ and that the two e.s.r. lines are equally intense.

The n.m.r. spectrum of molecules containing two coupled protons

Here $E_A^{(0)} = \frac{1}{2}\gamma\hbar B_z(1 - \sigma_A)$, $E_B^{(0)} = \frac{1}{2}\gamma\hbar B_z(1 - \sigma_B)$, $C_{AB} = J_{AB}$, and

$$K = (h/2)[\{(\gamma B_z/2\pi)(\sigma_A - \sigma_B)\}^2 + J_{AB}^2]^{\frac{1}{2}} = (h/2)(\delta_{AB}^2 + J_{AB}^2)^{\frac{1}{2}},$$

where δ_{AB} is the chemical shift. Both $E_A^{(0)}$ and $E_B^{(0)}$ are positive and the levels in increasing order of energy are 1, 2, 3, and 4. All four transitions occur with frequencies about the mean, $(E_A^{(0)} + E_B^{(0)})/h$, listed in Table 4. Since states 2 and 3 have mixed wave functions transitions involving them are neither completely of the A nor of the B nucleus; it is useful however to designate their origin in the first-order limit ($\delta_{AB} \gg J_{AB}$). The appearance of the spectrum alters considerably as the ratio δ/J is changed (Fig. 42), from the first-order spectrum to a single line when $\delta = 0$; between these limits the central lines of separation $(2K - J)$ move together and become intense, while the others lose intensity. The separation of the outer pairs of lines remains constant at J, but the chemical shift cannot be measured directly from the spectrum: it is calculated from the K value.

We see now that when $\delta = 0$ the coupling cannot be observed. This result may be obtained in more elegant fashion for when two nuclei are equivalent the eigenstates (2) and (3) must include equal contributions from $\alpha\beta$ and $\beta\alpha$,

TABLE 4

Transition	'Origin'	Frequency	Relative intensity
$4 \leftrightarrow 2$	A	$\frac{1}{2}J_{AB} + K/h$	$1 - \sin 2\theta$
$3 \leftrightarrow 1$	A	$-\frac{1}{2}J_{AB} + K/h$	$1 + \sin 2\theta$
$4 \leftrightarrow 3$	B	$\frac{1}{2}J_{AB} - K/h$	$1 + \sin 2\theta$
$2 \leftrightarrow 1$	B	$-\frac{1}{2}J_{AB} - K/h$	$1 - \sin 2\theta$

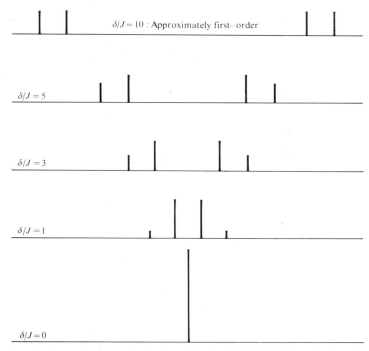

FIG. 42. The appearance of the n.m.r. spectrum of two coupled protons changes as the ratio of the chemical shift to the coupling constant is varied.

which occurs if $\cos \theta = \sin \theta = 2^{-\frac{1}{2}}$. The eigenstates are $\alpha\alpha$, $2^{-\frac{1}{2}}(\alpha\beta + \beta\alpha)$, $\beta\beta$ (whose sign is unchanged if the nuclei are interchanged and are termed symmetric), and $2^{-\frac{1}{2}}(\alpha\beta - \beta\alpha)$ (which is antisymmetric). The operator $\hat{P}_x$ induces transitions only between states of the same symmetry and so no transitions involving the antisymmetric level are allowed. The energies of the other three are simply $-2E_A^{(0)} + hJ/4$, $hJ/4$, and $2E_A^{(0)} + hJ/4$ and the frequency of both the transitions is $2E_A^{(0)}/h$, independent of J.

Extension to other systems

The methods of the foregoing sections are directly applicable to systems of more than two particles although complications arise: once more than one coupling occurs we have the problem that the coupling constants may differ in their relative signs, although the spectrum may show little change on various sign combinations (a high-resolution spectrum is invariant to a change in the absolute signs of all the coupling constants). Furthermore, computer

TABLE 5

1 $\nu_A + \frac{1}{2}J_{AM} + \frac{1}{2}J_{AX}$	5 $\nu_M + \frac{1}{2}J_{AM} + \frac{1}{2}J_{MX}$	9 $\nu_X + \frac{1}{2}J_{AX} + \frac{1}{2}J_{MX}$
2 $\nu_A + \frac{1}{2}J_{AM} - \frac{1}{2}J_{AX}$	6 $\nu_M + \frac{1}{2}J_{AM} - \frac{1}{2}J_{MX}$	10 $\nu_X + \frac{1}{2}J_{AX} - \frac{1}{2}J_{MX}$
3 $\nu_A - \frac{1}{2}J_{AM} + \frac{1}{2}J_{AX}$	7 $\nu_M - \frac{1}{2}J_{AM} + \frac{1}{2}J_{MX}$	11 $\nu_X - \frac{1}{2}J_{AX} + \frac{1}{2}J_{MX}$
4 $\nu_A - \frac{1}{2}J_{AM} - \frac{1}{2}J_{AX}$	8 $\nu_M - \frac{1}{2}J_{AM} - \frac{1}{2}J_{MX}$	12 $\nu_X - \frac{1}{2}J_{AX} - \frac{1}{2}J_{MX}$

Transition origins

1 $\alpha\beta\beta \leftrightarrow \beta\beta\beta$	5 $\beta\alpha\beta \leftrightarrow \beta\beta\beta$	9 $\beta\beta\alpha \leftrightarrow \beta\beta\beta$
2 $\alpha\beta\alpha \leftrightarrow \beta\beta\alpha$	6 $\beta\alpha\alpha \leftrightarrow \beta\beta\alpha$	10 $\beta\alpha\alpha \leftrightarrow \beta\alpha\beta$
3 $\alpha\alpha\beta \leftrightarrow \beta\alpha\beta$	7 $\alpha\alpha\beta \leftrightarrow \alpha\beta\beta$	11 $\alpha\beta\alpha \leftrightarrow \alpha\beta\beta$
4 $\alpha\alpha\alpha \leftrightarrow \beta\alpha\alpha$	8 $\alpha\alpha\alpha \leftrightarrow \alpha\beta\alpha$	12 $\alpha\alpha\alpha \leftrightarrow \alpha\alpha\beta$

solution of determinants such as (29) is entailed and not surprisingly many different solutions may be obtained: even for three nuclei four separate solutions are possible although two are usually imaginary. These solutions often differ in the relative signs of coupling constants and, if these can be determined independently, a unique solution can be obtained. For example, Table 5 lists the transition frequencies of a first-order n.m.r. system of three coupled nuclei (designated AMX: the letters, far apart in the alphabet, imply large chemical shift to coupling constant ratios between the nuclei); we write $\nu_A = (\gamma B_z/2\pi)(1 - \sigma_A)$ and henceforth assume that $\nu_A > \nu_M > \nu_X$ and $J_{MX} > J_{AM} > J_{AX}$. The corresponding spectrum is shown diagrammatically in Fig. 43 which shows that the identification of the lines with individual transitions changes if one of the coupling constants is of opposite sign to the others although the appearance of the spectrum does not. If we can identify the transitions in some independent experiment the signs of the coupling constants are determined. This is the province of the double resonance technique.

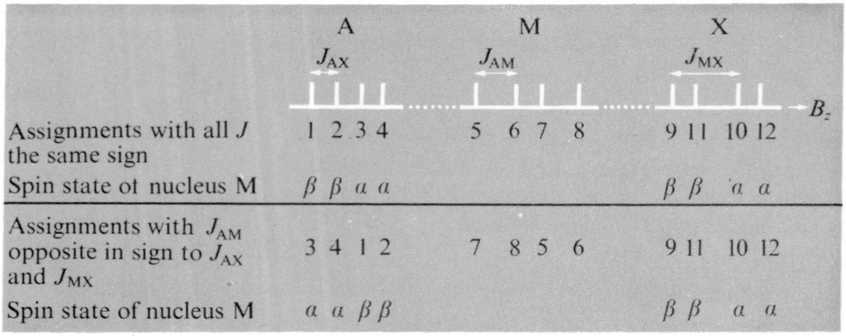

	A J_{AX}		M J_{AM}		X J_{MX}	
Assignments with all J the same sign	1 2 3 4		5 6 7 8		9 11 10 12	B_z
Spin state of nucleus M	$\beta\ \beta\ \alpha\ \alpha$				$\beta\ \beta\ \alpha\ \alpha$	
Assignments with J_{AM} opposite in sign to J_{AX} and J_{MX}	3 4 1 2		7 8 5 6		9 11 10 12	
Spin state of nucleus M	$\alpha\ \alpha\ \beta\ \beta$				$\beta\ \beta\ \alpha\ \alpha$	

FIG. 43. A diagrammatic first-order AMX spectrum due to three coupled protons; the identification of the lines with individual transitions alters if the relative signs of the coupling constants are varied.

Double resonance

The technique, applicable to e.s.r. and n.m.r., consists of satisfying the resonance conditions of two coupled particles simultaneously. Different radiofrequency field strengths are used at each : one perturbs either the energy levels or population differences set up by the applied field B_z, and its effect is monitored by the other. We shall discuss but a few of the many varieties of the experiment.

Spin decoupling

At its simplest this technique consists in irradiating one nucleus of a first-order two-nucleus (AX) system, and observing the effect on the doublet spectrum of the other. Under irradiation at its resonance frequency the nucleus A undergoes rapid transition from one state to the other with the result that the X nucleus, rather than 'sensing' it in one spin state or the other, senses only its average orientation. If the transition rate is high enough the spin coupling constant is averaged to zero and the doublet X spectrum collapses to a singlet of twice the intensity of each doublet component : the effect of spin coupling to A is removed from the system. The condition for this to happen is approximately that the irradiating field strength $\gamma B_2/2\pi > 2J$, but the field strength is an experimental variable set to produce maximum effect. The experiment has important uses in multinuclear situations in which a spectrum may be simplified considerably by removing from it all the couplings to one proton ; it can be used also to confirm whether or not two nuclei couple.

Its use in analysis is seen by reference to Fig. 43. We remember that the lines in a spectrum arise from different molecules. In particular we may consider the A and X parts of the spectrum to consist of the superposition of two AX subspectra arising from two separate types of molecule, one in which the M spin state is α, the other β (see the transition origins in Table 5 : in the first-order situation the basic product functions are eigenstates). We may perform a spin-decoupling experiment on either of the sets, independently of the other : within the AX spectrum of the α-set irradiation of the A doublet causes the corresponding X doublet to collapse, and similarly for the β-set. With all the coupling constants the same sign, irradiation of the low-field doublet of the A spectrum causes the low-field one of the X spectrum to collapse ; if J_{AM} is of opposite sign to J_{AX} and J_{MX} similar irradiation causes the high-field part of the X spectrum to collapse. An example is given in Fig. 44 which shows the spectrum of 2,3-dibromopropionic acid under spin decoupling ; the ^2J and ^3J couplings are of opposite sign.

Spin tickling

In this particular form of double resonance a much weaker irradiating field is used ($\gamma B_2/2\pi \sim$ line-width) and a single transition is irradiated.

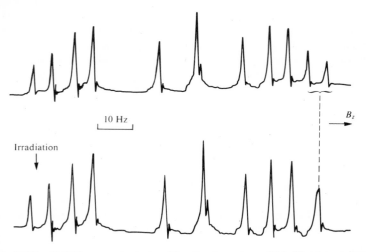

Fig. 44. The 60 MHz n.m.r. spectrum of the ethanic protons of 2,3-dibromopropionic acid, $CH_2BrCHBrCO_2H$, in benzene. It has $|^2J| = 9.9$ Hz and $|^3J| = 10.8$ Hz and 4.6 Hz. The central resonance has a triplet appearance due to unresolved lines. Irradiation of one half of an AX subspectrum as shown causes the other half to collapse into a singlet; this experiment compares the relative signs of the coupling constants not involved in the irradiation and shows ^2J to be of opposite sign to the 10.8 Hz ^3J coupling.

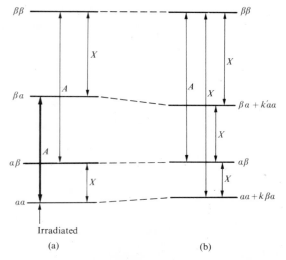

Fig. 45. The energy levels of an AX system (a) without 'tickling' and (b) with it.

Consider again the AX system with eigenstates $\alpha\alpha$, $\alpha\beta$, $\beta\alpha$, and $\beta\beta$ and A transitions $\alpha\alpha \leftrightarrow \beta\alpha$ and $\alpha\beta \leftrightarrow \beta\beta$, and X transitions $\alpha\alpha \leftrightarrow \alpha\beta$, and $\beta\alpha \leftrightarrow \beta\beta$; if the A transition $\alpha\alpha \leftrightarrow \beta\alpha$ is irradiated (Fig. 45) the states are perturbed and their new wave functions are of the form $(\alpha\alpha + k\beta\alpha)$ and $(\beta\alpha + k'\alpha\alpha)$, where k is some parameter (see Appendix).

Two new transitions of the X nucleus become allowed and instead of two lines, four are observed in the X region. An example, for a closely-coupled 'AB' system, is shown in Fig. 46. Each original X line is split into two equal components on tickling but the original A line is unaffected: as a general rule tickling only affects transitions that share a common energy level with the irradiated one. This allows the energy levels to be placed in their correct relative orders and once more yields the relative signs of coupling constants in multinuclear systems.

Spin tickling has found particular application in heteronuclear systems for it allows the spectrum of a nucleus coupled to a proton to be determined by irradiating it and observing the effect in the proton spectrum.

Electron-nuclear double resonance (ENDOR)

ENDOR differs from the forms already discussed in that a weak perturbing field is applied to a given transition solely to perturb the population difference of the levels between which it occurs (a similar technique INDOR is used in purely nuclear systems). To understand its application we refer to Fig. 41 which shows the e.s.r. transitions of the hydrogen atom; there are of course nuclear transitions which we may cause as well: $3 \leftrightarrow 1$ and $2 \leftrightarrow 4$. Suppose that while observing the e.s.r. spectrum we effect the $4 \leftrightarrow 2$ transition continuously: this tends to equalize the populations of the 2 and 4 levels and

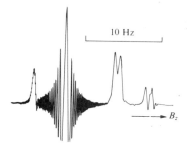

Fig. 46. The effect of 'tickling' one transition of an AB spectrum. This spectrum (of 2-bromo-5-chlorothiophene) has been run on a spectrometer which displays the spectrum by sweeping the frequency while keeping the magnetic field constant, and shows a beat pattern when the measurement frequency of the B_1 field approaches the frequency of the B_2 irradiating field. Frequency sweep greatly facilitates double resonance experiments.

causes their populations relative to the other levels to change; the $1 \leftrightarrow 2$ e.s.r. transition is weakened and the $3 \leftrightarrow 4$ one strengthened. The experiment is conducted slightly differently: one e.s.r. transition is saturated and a radio-frequency oscillator is swept through the nuclear region; whenever a nuclear transition occurs the e.s.r. one is un-saturated and observed. This allows transitions which share common energy levels to be identified, as in spin-tickling, and also gives very accurate values of hyperfine coupling constants, for n.m.r. lines are sharper than e.s.r. ones; the reader may verify that the separation in frequency of the two n.m.r. transitions, and therefore of the ENDOR lines, in hydrogen atoms is A_H.

ENDOR allows determination of hyperfine coupling constants which cannot be resolved in the e.s.r. spectrum and is useful in analysing complex spectra: the ENDOR spectrum simply consists in one pair of lines for each hyperfine coupling constant. For instance, the ENDOR spectrum of the anthracene anion consists of six lines, the e.s.r. spectrum of seventy-five.

7. The Solid State

OF the phenomena so far discussed, isotropic hyperfine and spin–spin coupled interactions occur via the electrons in a molecule and are independent of the phase of the sample. Anisotropic hyperfine interactions, dipolar couplings, screening constants, and g-factors are all anisotropic and in solution their average values are observed as the molecules tumble relative to the applied field direction; the first two average to zero. In a single crystal a molecule is constrained, at temperatures well below the melting point, in some particular orientation with respect to the crystal axes and its spectrum changes as the crystal is rotated inside the applied field. The spectrum contains more information than does that of the same molecule in solution although it is not possible always to extract it.

The screening constants of protons in molecules have too small anisotropies to be observed in solids and little attention has been given to other nuclei. Similarly the g-factors of organic radicals are only slightly anisotropic although the anisotropy is accentuated if the electron is localized at an inorganic atom. An example of the latter, and also of the existence of anisotropic hyperfine interaction, is provided by nitroxide radicals.

Nitroxide radicals

The unpaired electron in nitroxides is located largely in a nitrogen $2p$ orbital. The isotropic hyperfine interaction observed in solution originates in a spin-polarization mechanism but in the solid an anisotropic hyperfine coupling occurs also, directly between the electron and the nucleus. As discussed in Chapter 5, this is a 'through space' dipolar effect in which each particle causes a field at the other, according to equation (16), which depends upon the angle between the applied field and the radius vector connecting the two: although we must average the interaction over the p-orbital, the resultant coupling is angle-dependent. The same is true of the g-factor (p. 39). Fig. 47 shows the effect of rotating a single crystal of tetramethyl-1,3-cyclobutanedione containing a small quantity of di-t-butyl nitroxide about the field direction; the dilute crystal is used to minimize inter-radical effects. Knowing the crystal structure, it is possible to orient the radical in specific directions and the figure shows spectra obtained with the field along the N—O bond (the x-axis), along the $2p$-orbital axis (the y-axis) and along the direction perpendicular to these two (the z-axis). The centre of the spectrum is seen to shift and analysis gives $g_{xx} = 2.00872$, $g_{yy} = 2.00616$, and $g_{zz} = 2.00270$; the triplet spacing due to coupling to spin-1 ^{14}N varies also: $A_{xx} = 21.27$ MHz, $A_{yy} = 16.67$ MHz, $A_{zz} = 89.06$ MHz. These couplings are the sum of the isotropic and anisotropic hyperfine contributions.

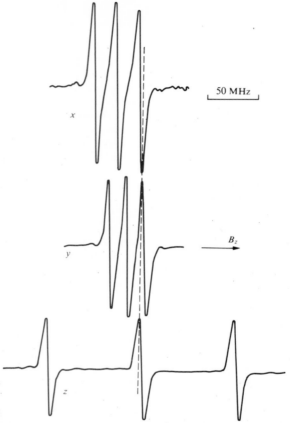

FIG. 47. The e.s.r. spectra of di-t-butyl nitroxide in a host single crystal of tetra-methyl-1,3-cyclobutanedione with B_z along the x-, y-, and z-directions (see text). Note that both the position and the splitting of the resonance change as the crystal is reoriented. The broken line corresponds to $g = 2.0036$.

Nitroxide radicals are unusually stable and exist in great variety; they find wide use in biology as *spin labels*. In this application a nitroxide analogue of a biological molecule is synthesized to have its nitroxide group at a known rigid orientation with respect to a molecular axis and is incorporated into a living system, or a model of one. Small concentrations of radical are required for detection in a diamagnetic environment and little perturbation of the system is caused. An example is the use of phospholipid molecules synthesized with nitroxide groups held in planar rings perpendicular to their long axes

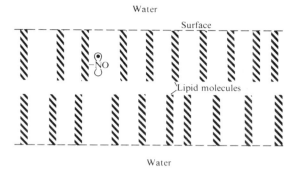

FIG. 48. A diagrammatic representation of a lipid bi-layer containing a spin-labelled phospholipid molecule.

to investigate the lipid bi-layer structure of cell walls (Fig. 48). If a bi-layer containing nitroxide is oriented with its surface perpendicular to the applied field of an e.s.r. spectrometer a spectrum is observed with a splitting A_{yy}, which implies that the p-orbital axis, and therefore the molecular axis, is perpendicular to the surface. When the surface is re-oriented along the field direction, in some systems an average coupling $\frac{1}{2}(A_{xx}+A_{zz})$ is observed, which implies that the phospholipid rotates freely about its long axis, and in others individual components A_{xx} and A_{zz} can be observed separately, depending on the motion involved. The amount of motion can be varied by adding cholesterol to the layer or, very interestingly, by the action of anaesthetics although not, as yet, at physiologically-meaningful concentrations.

Dipolar interactions

In a solid, two magnetic particles i and j produce dipolar fields at each other according to equation (16); in an ensemble two different local fields result at each, from the two different orientations of the magnetic moment, and two magnetic resonance conditions arise: a doublet spectrum is expected for each with a separation equal to $\mu_0\mu(i)\mu(j)(3\cos^2\theta-1)/4\pi r^3 h$ Hz. This simple classical picture gives the correct result provided that i and j are inequivalent; if they are equivalent a quantum approach is necessary (this gives the correct result for the inequivalent case also, of course).

The full classical equation for the interaction energy of two dipoles is

$$(\mu_0/4\pi r^3)[\mathbf{\mu}(i)\,.\,\mathbf{\mu}(j)-3\{\mathbf{\mu}(i)\,.\,\mathbf{r}\}\{\mathbf{\mu}(j)\,.\,\mathbf{r}\}/r^2];$$

its operator form is consequently

$$(\mu_0 g_i\mu_i g_j\mu_j/4\pi r^3\hbar^2)[\hat{\mathbf{P}}(i)\,.\,\hat{\mathbf{P}}(j)-3(\hat{\mathbf{P}}(i)\,.\,\mathbf{r})\{\hat{\mathbf{P}}(j)\,.\,\mathbf{r}\}/r^2],$$

where μ_i and μ_j are either μ_B or μ_N according as to the identity of the particles. This can be simplified by expanding the products and transforming to spherical polar coordinates (see standard texts); the main contribution to the energy operator is of the form

$$(4\pi^2 T_{ij}/h)[\hat{P}_z(i)\hat{P}_z(j) - \tfrac{1}{4}\{\hat{P}^+(i)\hat{P}^-(j) + \hat{P}^-(i)\hat{P}^+(j)\}]$$

where T_{ij}, the dipolar coupling constant, is $\mu_0 g_i \mu_i g_j \mu_j (1 - 3\cos^2\theta)/4\pi h r^3$ Hz.

The energy operator $\hat{H}^{(1)}$ (equation (26)) in the presence of dipolar coupling and isotropic coupling, with a coupling constant C_{ij}, is

$$\hat{H}^{(1)} = (4\pi^2/h)\sum_{i<j}[(C_{ij} + T_{ij})\hat{P}_z(i)\hat{P}_z(j) + \tfrac{1}{4}(2C_{ij} - T_{ij})\{\hat{P}^+(i)\hat{P}^-(j) + \hat{P}^-(i)\hat{P}^+(j)\}].$$

$$(30)$$

In first-order cases, such as the mutual coupling of inequivalent nuclei or an electron and a nucleus, only the first term in this equation yields a non-zero energy: the dipolar coupling produces no new splitting in the spectrum but merely causes its magnitude to change from the isotropic value C_{ij} to $(C_{ij} + T_{ij})$. If two equivalent particles are considered, however, an extra term originating in the second part of the equation does cause extra splitting; we consider this in n.m.r. below. In the former situation whether the solid spectrum of a molecule resembles its solution one or not depends upon the relative magnitudes of the dipolar and isotropic couplings: it is instructive to calculate T_{ij}.

Electron–nucleus dipolar couplings in e.s.r.

For an electron 0·1 nm away from a proton $|T_{ij}| = 79·04|(3\cos^2\theta - 1)|$ MHz, which may be of the same order as A_α, the hyperfine coupling constant between an electron and a proton attached to an α-carbon atom. The observed splitting in the solid-state e.s.r. spectrum consequently depends critically on the angle between the electron-nucleus vector and the applied field, as demonstrated in Fig. 49 which shows that the splitting observed in the radical $\cdot CH(COOH)_2$ (produced by irradiating malonic acid with X-rays) changes as the crystal is rotated relative to the applied field. The fact that a single doublet is observed in each of the orientations shown implies that all the radicals have the same orientation in this particular crystal; often cases are encountered where two or more occur and the spectrum is the superposition of the individual spectrum of each. The width of the lines should be noted and compared with those observed in solution (in Fig. 13, for instance): the extra width in the solid originates in unresolved dipolar interactions to other protons. Study of the variation in splitting as the crystal is rotated allows both the isotropic coupling constant and the components of the dipole coupling tensor to be extracted, the latter relative to the axes of the crystal. If the structure of the crystal is known the principal components

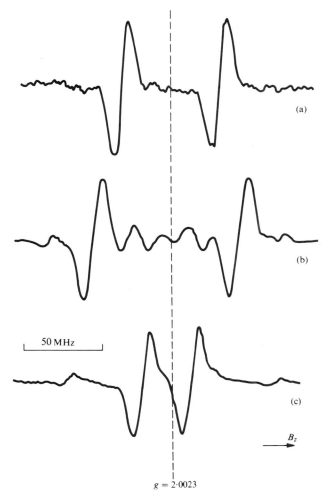

50 MHz

B_z

$g = 2 \cdot 0023$

FIG. 49. The e.s.r. spectrum of a single crystal of malonic acid containing the radical ·CH(COOH)$_2$ as the crystal is rotated relative to the field direction with B_z parallel (a) to the crystal x-axis, (b) to the y-axis, and (c) to the z-axis.

of the coupling tensor in the molecule can be obtained; conversely if the latter are known, or can be guessed, the crystal structure is elucidated with the assumption, almost always justified, that the free radical occupies one of the normal lattice positions in the crystal.

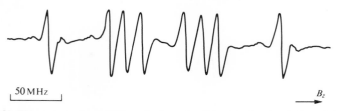

50 MHz B_z

FIG. 50. The e.s.r. spectrum of the radical produced in a single crystal of succinic acid by X-irradiation, at a particular orientation in the field.

Since the dipolar coupling depends upon $1/r^3$ it falls off rapidly with distance and is very small for electrons coupling to protons attached to β-carbon atoms, for which however the isotropic coupling A_β is large (p. 66), β-couplings are therefore dominated by the isotropic term. The principle use of solid-state e.s.r. spectra is to identify the radical produced when a crystal is irradiated with light, X-, or γ-radiation. An example is given in Fig. 50; this spectrum was obtained from X-irradiated succinic acid at one particular orientation of the crystal relative to the field. It shows the eight lines expected of three inequivalent couplings to protons and identifies the radical as $\cdot CH(COOH)CH_2COOH$; the β-couplings are isotropic and unequal (80·08 MHz and 101·0 MHz), which implies that the molecule adopts an unsymmetrical conformation in the crystal (p. 66).

Electron–electron dipolar couplings: fine structure in e.s.r. spectra

Some species contain more than one unpaired electron and exhibit the phenomenon of fine structure in their e.s.r. spectra; these include triplet state molecules and transition metal ions.

Triplet states

Both triplet molecules and bi-radicals contain two unpaired electrons, but whereas in the latter they are quite independent, in the former their spin angular momenta couple to give a resultant $S = \sum_i s(i)$ where $S = 1$. Bi-radicals, such as a polymer chain growing by a radical mechanism at each end, exhibit normal e.s.r. spectra which are the superpositions of those for each electron. With triplets the observable components of the spin angular momenta are $m_S \hbar$ where $m_S = \pm 1, 0$ and there are three non-degenerate states in an applied field, between which transitions may occur. Their energies (from equations (2) and (7), using observable values) are $g_e \mu_B B_z m_S$ and they are equally separated: the two transitions have equal energy and one e.s.r. line should be observed. In practice two lines are obtained and the spectrum is said to exhibit fine structure; it originates in dipolar interactions between the electrons, which occur even in the absence of an applied field: the energy levels have a *zero-field splitting*.

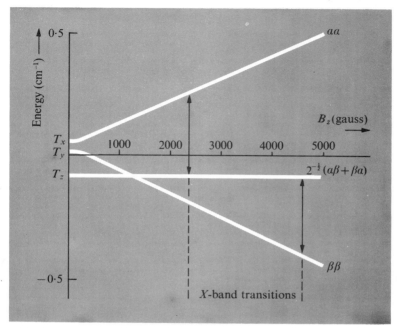

FIG. 51. The field dependence of the triplet energy levels of naphthalene when the field is applied perpendicularly to the plane of the molecule.

The resultant energy of the states can be calculated by the methods of Chapter 6 using the $\hat{H}^{(0)}$ expression given there and the operator form of the dipolar coupling given in the last section. Here we only indicate some features of the calculation. Starting from the basic symmetric triplet wave functions $\alpha\alpha$, $2^{-\frac{1}{2}}(\alpha\beta+\beta\alpha)$ and $\beta\beta$, we construct a new set referred to the x-, y-, and z-axes of the molecule: $T_x = 2^{-\frac{1}{2}}(\beta\beta-\alpha\alpha)$, $T_y = i2^{-\frac{1}{2}}(\alpha\alpha+\beta\beta)$, $T_z = 2^{-\frac{1}{2}}(\alpha\beta+\beta\alpha)$. For example, in the triplet state of naphthalene we define the z-axis perpendicular to the plane of the molecule, the x-axis along the bond joining the two rings, and the y-axis perpendicular to these in the plane of the molecule. A magnetic field applied in the z-direction leaves T_z an eigenstate but mixes T_x and T_y; solution of the secular equations yields the eigenstates $\psi_x = \cos\theta(\alpha\alpha)-\sin\theta(\beta\beta)$, $\psi_y = \sin\theta(\alpha\alpha)+\cos\theta(\beta\beta)$. The field dependence of the energies of all three states for naphthalene is shown in Fig. 51; the eigenstates become T_x, T_y, and T_z at zero field and the basic triplet ones at high field, where the dipolar coupling is negligible compared with the energies of the electrons in the applied field. The energy of T_z, for which $m_S = 0$, is independent of the field. At high field the selection rule is $\Delta m_S = \pm 1$ and two lines appear asymmetrically about 3300 G, the position of a $g = 2.0023$ radical at X-band, and in general they have different intensities. Interestingly, at intermediate fields the operator $\hat{P}_z$ ($\equiv \hat{s}_z$ here) has a non-zero matrix element between ψ_x and ψ_y, as the reader may verify from the wave functions, and a $m_S = \pm 2$, 'double quantum' transition can be induced by applying a varying B_1 field *parallel* to the applied field direction. Two different energy diagrams like Fig. 51 are obtained if the field is applied in the x- and y-directions.

Some molecules, chiefly derivatives of methylene and nitrene, such as diphenylmethylene and phenyl nitrene, are triplets in their ground states. Others have long-lived molecular excited states which may be produced in the cavity of an e.s.r. spectrometer by continuous irradiation; an example is naphthalene held in a host durene crystal in a dilute form to prevent energy exchange between adjacent naphthalene molecules. Analysis of the fine structure of its spectrum shows that the zero-field splitting causes its upper levels to lie 2611 MHz ($0.0871 \, \mathrm{cm}^{-1}$) and 3457 MHz ($0.1153 \, \mathrm{cm}^{-1}$) above the lowest. Transitions may be induced between these zero-field levels: e.s.r. without a magnet.

Triplet spectra are expected to exhibit hyperfine structure also but few examples are known; triplet naphthalene is one of them. In solution rapid relaxation usually precludes even their detection.

Transition metal ions

Zero-field splitting leads to fine structure in the spectra of transition metal ions also, but its origin is rarely dipolar interaction since another effect, spin–orbit coupling, dominates. According to the familiar perturbation theory expression, this interaction changes the energies of the lowest-lying d-orbitals in a crystal by an amount proportional to

$$\sum_n \left\langle \psi_0 \left| \sum_i \hat{\mathbf{l}}(i) \cdot \hat{\mathbf{s}}(i) \right| \psi_n \right\rangle \left\langle \psi_n \left| \sum_i \hat{\mathbf{l}}(i) \cdot \hat{\mathbf{s}}(i) \right| \psi_0 \right\rangle.$$

On the assumption that the space part of each wave function is separate from the spin part, expansion of this expression gives terms in $\mathbf{s}(i) \cdot \mathbf{s}(j)$, representing spin coupling between the electrons similar in form to that discussed in the dipolar interaction case above. If the ground state is initially degenerate, the effect of spin–orbit coupling on the energies of each degenerate state may differ and the degeneracy be wholly or partially removed.

The zero-field splittings in crystals of transition metal compounds may be extremely large. Thus for V^{3+} with a $3d^2$ electron configuration, the splitting between the ground and two degenerate upper levels is 239·8 GHz and no e.s.r. transition can be observed using X-band (9·6 GHz) equipment at feasible operating field strengths.

The e.s.r. spectra of crystals containing transition metal ions form a complex subject in their own right and each example must be considered individually; we have sought to indicate only some of the principles involved.

Nucleus–nucleus dipolar couplings in n.m.r.

For two protons separated by 0.1 nm, $|T_{ij}| = 120.11|(3\cos^2\theta - 1)|$ kHz; J_{ij} is of the order of 10 Hz and so the splittings in the n.m.r. spectrum of a molecule in the solid state are dominated completely by the dipolar term. T_{ij} may also be much greater than the chemical shift although it happens that most of the crystal studies have been performed on molecules containing equivalent nuclei. We consider the situation where there are two equivalent nuclei, as is found in the water molecules in hydrate crystals; we use the basic symmetric triplet levels once more and neglect the isotropic coupling in the energy operator $\hat{H}^{(1)}$ (equation (30)). The energies of the $\alpha\alpha$, $2^{-\frac{1}{2}}(\alpha\beta + \beta\alpha)$, and $\beta\beta$ states are simply shown to be $-2E_A^{(0)} + \frac{1}{4}hT_{AA}$, $-\frac{1}{2}hT_{AA}$ and $2E_A^{(0)} + \frac{1}{4}hT_{AA}$ respectively. In contrast to the solution spectrum the two transitions occur at different frequencies, separated by $\frac{3}{2}T_{AA}$ Hz. This is just $\frac{3}{2}$ times the splitting predicted classically.

An early example of the n.m.r. spectrum of water in the solid state in a single crystal of gypsum, $CaSO_4 \cdot 2H_2O$, is shown in Fig. 52 as the crystal is rotated relative to the field direction. The two water molecules occupy inequivalent positions in the unit cell and in some orientations yield separate doublet spectra; when $(3\cos^2\theta - 1) = 0$ (at $\theta = 54° 44'$) the dipolar coupling is zero. The crystal structure of gypsum is known and it is possible to interpret the angles between the crystal axes and the applied field in terms of the corresponding angles between the inter-proton vectors and the applied field, which allows the inter-proton distance to be calculated from the measured splitting. For gypsum $T_{AA}/(3\cos^2\theta - 1) = 45.98$ kHz and $r = 0.158$ nm.

The great width of the lines should be noted: in solution water has a line-width (controlled by exchange processes) of about 1 Hz. The width

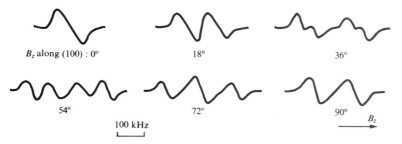

B_z along (100) : 0°   18°   36°

54°   72°   90°
                                                                              B_z
                         100 kHz
                         ⊢——————⊣

FIG. 52. The broad-line n.m.r. spectrum of a single crystal of gypsum as it is rotated relative to the field direction; note the extreme width of the lines.

originates in unresolved dipolar couplings to all the other protons in the crystal each of which produces its own contribution to the local dipolar field. The main application of solid state n.m.r. is to determine inter-proton distances, which otherwise are available only from neutron scattering experiments or X-ray difference maps, and it might be thought that the line-width would preclude great accuracy. This problem can be overcome analytically by a 'second moment' analysis of the line shape. We define the second moment of a line as its mean square width $\overline{(\Delta v)^2}$ measured from the centre of the line at a frequency v^*: it can be evaluated graphically from the observed line. Mathematically it is given by

$$\overline{(\Delta v)^2} = \int_0^\infty (v - v^*)^2 g(v)\, dv \Big/ \int_0^\infty g(v)\, dv,$$

where $g(v)$ describes the line-shape. This expression may be calculated for a specific model: we assume that the line shape is Gaussian and that the local fields which cause line-broadening arise from n protons in equivalent positions. This yields the Van Vleck equation

$$\overline{(\Delta v)^2} = \{3\mu_0^2\gamma^4\hbar^2 I(I+1)/256\pi^4 n\} \sum_j (1 - 3\cos^2\theta_{ij})^2/r_{ij}^6.$$

Summation is over all the protons within the crystal. This method gives remarkably accurate values of interproton distances: in benzene a value of 0.2495 ± 0.0018 nm is obtained, which compares well with the X-ray measurement (0.2473 ± 0.0025 nm).

A study of the spectrum of benzene as a function of temperature shows an abrupt change in line-width around 90 K; this is interpreted as the onset of molecular rotation on the lattice points. A similar phenomenon in cyclohexane a little below its melting point is due to the molecules migrating through the lattice.

Partially-oriented molecules

The second moment calculation is possible only for certain simple systems, which prevents derivation of internuclear distances for many molecules. This problem has been overcome in recent years by observing the dipolar interactions of nuclei not in the solid state but in solution in some remarkable highly-oriented fluid phases of liquid crystals. These are materials, such as 4,4'-di-n-hexyloxy-azoxybenzene, which upon melting exhibit one or more intermediate phases between the solid and the normal isotropic melt. The phase of particular use in n.m.r. is the nematic which, on inspection, is found to be turbid. The opacity results from large swarms of molecules (typically 10^4 or more), which are held together by strong lateral intermolecular forces between the rod-shaped molecules, and each swarm is oriented randomly with respect to every other one. When introduced into a strong magnetic field,

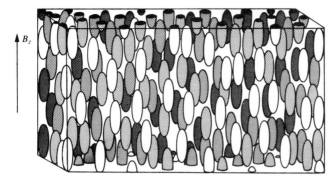

FIG. 53. The orientation of the molecules in a nematic phase inside the applied field.

as in an n.m.r. spectrometer, the swarms align with their long axes along the field direction causing the molecules to align too, with a high degree of orientation. This happens because the swarms of molecules have large magnetic anisotropies: the applied field induces a magnetic moment in the swarm which causes the molecule axes to orient parallel to the field (Fig. 53). The anisotropy of a single molecule is too small for it to be aligned on its own (the thermal energy is greater than the magnetic energy); the phenomenon is a cooperative one. The nematic phase is similar to a solid in that the molecular axes have specific orientations but it differs in the all-important aspect that the molecules are in continuous translational relative motion with respect to each other. This motion suffices to average to zero all intermolecular dipolar interactions. The n.m.r. spectrum observed is consequently essentially that of a set of isolated oriented molecules.

The liquid-crystalline materials themselves contain many inequivalent protons which couple to give a great number of transitions with the result that each is unresolvable and only a rather broad envelope is observed. It is possible however to dissolve small molecules in these phases; they become oriented by intermolecular forces and their spectra show dipolar splittings; their transitions are observed as sharp lines superimposed on the broad background spectrum of the liquid crystal itself. The motional averaging is so effective that the line-widths are comparable to those of normal high-resolution spectra, although purely technical limitations of maintaining temperature homogeneity throughout the sample tends to broaden them in practice. An example, the spectrum of 1,3,5-trichlorobenzene, is given in Fig. 54; it is a 1:2:1 triplet with line separation $\frac{3}{2}T_{HH}$ Hz, because the protons are equivalent. Here we encounter a difficulty, for we do not know how perfectly the solute orients; the observed splitting depends on the average $\overline{(3\cos^2\theta - 1)}$ in the medium which, knowing that the protons are in a plane perpendicular to the

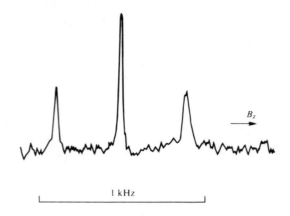

B_z

⊢————— 1 kHz —————⊣

FIG. 54. The nematic phase 60 MHz n.m.r. spectrum of 1,3,5-trichlorobenzene in solution in 4,4′-di-n-hexyloxy-azoxybenzene at 353 K. The normal n.m.r. spectrum is a single line since the protons are equivalent.

threefold axis of the molecule, we can express relative to the orientation of the axis and the applied field: if these are at an angle ϕ, $\theta = (90 + \phi)$ and $\cos^2\theta = \cos^2\phi$. We define an orientation parameter $S_3 = \frac{1}{2}(3\cos^2\phi - 1)$ and re-write the observed splitting in the form $3T^{(0)}S_3/r_{HH}^3 \equiv 360.33\, S_3/r_{HH}^3$ kHz, where $T^{(0)} = \mu_0 g_H^2 \mu_N^2/4\pi h$. In this molecule $r_{HH} = 0.43$ nm and $S_3 = 0.153$ in the particular liquid crystal at the particular temperature shown in Fig. 54. One use of both n.m.r. and e.s.r. spectra in liquid crystals is to investigate the motion in the phase, and hence the intermolecular forces, through the S parameters; an axially symmetric molecule requires one to define its average orientation, a C_{2v} molecule, three (one with respect to each axis) and an unsymmetric one, five.

Molecular geometry

Cylindrical methyl derivatives, such as CH_3CN, yield a similar triplet spectrum which is further split into two if a ^{13}C nucleus is inserted in the methyl group. The isotropic coupling J_{CH} is too large to be neglected (136.5 Hz) and the observed splitting is $|T_{CH} + J_{CH}|$. (This implies that if the sign of T_{CH} is known, that is if the direction of the molecular orientation is known, the absolute sign of J_{CH} can be deduced from the observed splitting; the method used originally was to orient a polar molecule in an applied electric field, which necessitates no speculation as to its orientation direction.) Both T_{CH} and T_{HH} depend upon the same orientation parameter, that of the molecular axis, although the C—H and H—H vectors are at different angles with respect to it. By taking their ratio the S_3 parameter is eliminated and it is easy to show from geometry, and because T_{CH} occurs between inequivalent nuclei, that,

$$\frac{T_{CH}}{T_{HH}} = \frac{2}{3} \frac{\gamma_c}{\gamma_H} \left(\frac{r_{HH}}{r_{CH}}\right)^3 \left(\frac{r_{HH}^2}{r_{CH}^2} - 2\right).$$

From this (r_{HH}/r_{CH}) is evaluated and the bond angle in the methyl group is simply $2 \sin^{-1}(r_{HH}/r_{CH})$. Extremely good agreement is found with microwave values and the accuracy is comparable. (Note, however, that the n.m.r. result depends on the average value $\overline{(1/r^3)}$, and the microwave result on $\overline{(1/r^2)}$: these differ.)

This technique promises to be particularly useful in determining the structures of inorganic molecules containing protons and heavy atoms for the latter make observation of X-ray diffraction from the hydrogen atoms almost impossible. An example is π-cyclopentadienyl manganese tricarbonyl shown, with its spectrum in solution in a liquid crystal which has a nematic phase at the temperature of a normal n.m.r. sample, in Fig. 55. This molecule has

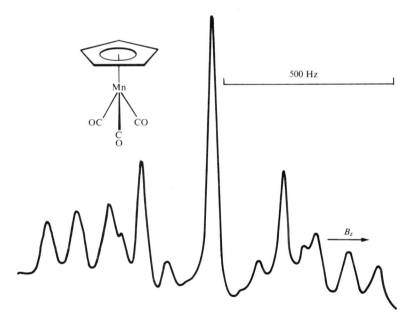

FIG. 55. The nematic phase 60 MHz spectrum and structure of π-cyclopentadienyl manganese tricarbonyl in a mixture of 43·5 per cent n-pentyl, 36·5 per cent n-butyl derivatives of $RCOO \cdot C_6H_4 \cdot N = N \cdot C_6H_4 OEt$, and 20 per cent of 4-$p$-n-nonyloxy-benzylidene-amino-3-bromobiphenyl at 310 K. The unusual width of the lines originates in effects from the spin $\frac{5}{2}$ Mn nucleus.

a unique axis and extensive X-ray investigations on the molecular type suggest that the carbon ring is approximately a regular planar pentagon. Assuming that the hydrogens are in the same plane and also assuming reasonable C—H bond lengths, we expect the spectrum to depend on a single geometrical parameter $(r_{12}/r_{13})^3 = 4.24$; for the precise X-ray geometry of this particular molecule 4.312 would be expected. Experimentally it is found that the spectrum can be calculated using one single geometric parameter but that its value is 4.07 ± 0.04, which is incompatible with the X-ray results. It seems very probable that the molecule has a dynamic structure in which some of the protons, and probably the carbon atoms, are out of the plane of the others at any one time. It cannot be static for the normal high-resolution spectrum is a single sharp line. The X-ray result is obtained from measurements over a long period of time and is insensitive to such a time-average effect.

Anisotropy of screening constants

Although the dipolar couplings in nematic phases are large (kHz in methyl compounds) and may dominate chemical shifts between inequivalent nuclei, the lines are sharp and their positions may be measured accurately. The screening constant tensor is not spherically averaged but for a molecule with a cylindrically symmetric tensor, $\bar{\sigma} = \sigma + \frac{2}{3}(\sigma_{\parallel} - \sigma_{\perp})S_3$, where σ is the isotropic value. Its effect on the spectrum is calculated by re-writing the operator $\hat{H}^{(0)}$ to include the anisotropic term: it causes a measurable shift in the resonance position. In proton systems there is considerable evidence that the values obtained for the anisotropy are affected by the medium but in fluorine compounds the effect is larger and the derived values trustworthy.

Finally, the complexity of nematic phase spectra deserves comment. Benzene, which shows a single high-resolution line, yields a spectrum of seventy-eight lines in the nematic phase. Interpretation shows it to be a regular planar hexagon!

Appendix: Operators, Matrix Elements, and Perturbation Theory

A n operator is a short-hand notation for what may be a complex mathematical operation; it acts on a function and transforms it into another. Thus an operator d/dx transforms x^2 to $2x$; an operator $x \times$ transforms $f(x)$ to $xf(x)$. In quantum mechanics the wave function ψ represents the state of a system while its observable properties are described by operators: the equation $\hat{Z}\psi = z\psi$ states that an operation represented by the operator $\hat{Z}$ performed on a system produces the result z, the eigenvalue. Writing one of the wave functions of an electron in an applied field α (Chapter 6), the equation $\hat{P}_z\alpha = \frac{1}{2}\hbar\alpha$ implies that the measurable component of its angular momentum in this state is $\frac{1}{2}\hbar$.

An operator equation may be written for the energy also: $\hat{H}\Psi = E\Psi$ where the energy operator $\hat{H}$ is called the Hamiltonian of the system. Often Ψ is written as a linear combination of the wave functions of states, $\sum_i C_i\psi_i$, where the ψ_i individually satisfy the operator equation; when this is done the energy equation is solved conveniently by multiplying through by the complex conjugate of each wave function in turn, to produce i equations, and integrating. A typical equation is

$$\int \psi_1^* \hat{H} \sum_i c_i\psi_i \, d\tau = E \int \psi_1^* \sum_i c_i\psi_i \, d\tau.$$

This contains terms such as $\int \psi_m^* \hat{H} \psi_n \, d\tau$ and $\int \psi_m^* \psi_n \, d\tau$ which are written often in the Dirac bra and ket notation, $\langle\psi_m|\hat{H}|\psi_n\rangle$, and $\langle\psi_m|\psi_n\rangle$ respectively. If the wave functions are normalized and orthogonal $\langle\psi_m|\psi_n\rangle = 1$ if $m = n$ and is zero otherwise: the equation above becomes

$$c_1\langle\psi_1|\hat{H}|\psi_1\rangle + c_2\langle\psi_1|\hat{H}|\psi_2\rangle + \dots + c_i\langle\psi_1|\hat{H}|\psi_i\rangle = E_1 c_1.$$

The i equations of this type are conveniently written in matrix form (see for example Chapter 6) and the individual terms $\langle\psi_m|\hat{H}|\psi_n\rangle$ are known as matrix elements of the Hamiltonian $\hat{H}$; they are given the symbol H_{mn}.

It is not often possible to solve the energy equation exactly although that may be possible for a model system which closely approximates the real one. In perturbation theory we write an operator $\hat{H} = \hat{H}^{(0)} + \lambda\hat{H}^{(1)} + \lambda^2\hat{H}^{(2)} + \dots$, where λ is some small quantity which represents the importance of successive terms. We solve the problem using the model operator $\hat{H}^{(0)}$ only and examine the effect of the other terms on the wave functions and energies it produces. The series may be terminated where desired: after the first term in λ the theory is called *first-order*, after the second, *second-order*. The general theory is treated in standard texts; the wave function corrected to first order is

$$\psi_i = \psi_i^{(0)} - \sum_j' \left(\frac{\langle \psi_j^{(0)} | \hat{H}^{(1)} | \psi_i^{(0)} \rangle}{E_j^{(0)} - E_i^{(0)}} \right) \psi_j^{(0)},$$

where $\sum_j'$ represents summation over all the states j; the energy to second order is

$$E_i = E_i^{(0)} + \langle \psi_i^{(0)} | \hat{H}^{(1)} | \psi_i^{(0)} \rangle - \sum_j' \frac{\langle \psi_i^{(0)} | \hat{H}^{(1)} | \psi_j^{(0)} \rangle \langle \psi_j^{(0)} | \hat{H}^{(1)} | \psi_i^{(0)} \rangle}{E_j^{(0)} - E_i^{(0)}},$$

where the superscript (0) refers to the model system.

Perturbation theory is particularly useful in magnetic resonance for all the interactions, whether between particles or with field, are small compared with electron orbital energies. Angular momentum operators mix ground and higher states of a system and consequently yield zero values for the first perturbation term in the energy equation; g-factors, screening constants, and coupling constants all must be calculated using second-order theory.

Bibliography and Notes

A LIST of references is provided for the reader who may wish to enquire more deeply into the topics discussed in this volume. It is intended both to define some of the major textbooks in the subject and also to provide suitable undergraduate reading. Some general texts are given first followed by specific references to subjects discussed in the chapters; for the most part one reference only is given to each topic and further ones may be found by reference to it; for this reason usually the most recent is given.

General texts

P. W. ATKINS (1970) *Molecular quantum mechanics*. Clarendon Press, Oxford. This is concerned both with the basic theory of quantum mechanics and of approximation methods, and with the theory of magnetic interactions. It is written in SI units.

A. CARRINGTON and A. D. MCLACHLAN (1967) *Introduction to magnetic resonance*. Harper and Row, New York. An exposition of the theory of magnetic resonance in many of its applications.

C. P. SLICHTER (1963) *Principles of magnetic resonance*. Harper and Row, New York. A source text of advanced level.

H. G. HECHT (1967) *Magnetic resonance spectroscopy*. Wiley, New York.

J. S. WAUGH (editor) *Advances in magnetic resonance*. Academic Press, New York. A review series published almost annually.

n.m.r. texts

A. ABRAGAM (1961) *The principles of nuclear magnetism*. Clarendon Press, Oxford. The major textbook of the physics of the phenomenon.

R. M. LYNDEN-BELL and R. K. HARRIS (1969) *Nuclear magnetic resonance spectroscopy*. Nelson, London. SI units and the best introduction to the subject.

J. A. POPLE, W. G. SCHNEIDER, and H. J. BERNSTEIN (1959) *High-resolution nuclear magnetic resonance*. McGraw-Hill, New York.

J. W. EMSLEY, J. FEENEY, and L. H. SUTCLIFFE (1965) *High-resolution nuclear magnetic resonance spectroscopy*. Pergamon Press, Oxford. An encyclopaedic account of the work to that date.

J. W. EMSLEY, J. FEENEY, and L. H. SUTCLIFFE (editors) *Progress in nuclear magnetic resonance spectroscopy*. Pergamon Press, Oxford. A review series, published frequently.

L. M. JACKMAN and S. STERNHELL (1969) *Applications of nuclear magnetic resonance spectroscopy in organic chemistry*. Pergamon Press, Oxford.

E. F. MOONEY (editor) *Annual review of NMR spectroscopy*. Academic Press, New York.

P. DIEHL, E. FLUCK, and R. KOSFELD *N M R: basic principles and progress*. Springer-Verlag, New York. A review series.

e.s.r. texts

P. B. AYSCOUGH (1967) *Electron spin resonance in chemistry*. Methuen, London.

G. E. PAKE (1960) *Paramagnetic resonance*. Benjamin, New York. Deals specifically with transition metal ions and relaxation.

A. ABRAGAM and B. BLEANEY (1970) *Electron paramagnetic resonance of transition ions.* Clarendon Press, Oxford. The reference text in the subject.
C. P. POOLE (1967) *Electron spin resonance.* Interscience, New York. Experimental technology.

Chapter 1

Relaxation theory. A. G. REDFIELD (1965) *Adv. magn. Reson.* **1**, 1. An advanced treatise.

Chapter 2

e.s.r. of radical ions. A. CARRINGTON (1963) *Q. Rev. chem. Soc.* **17**, 67; K. BOWERS (1965) *Adv. magn. Reson.* **1**, 317.
e.s.r. of unstable radicals. R. O. C. NORMAN and B. C. GILBERT (1967) *Adv. phys. org. Chem.* **5**, 53. Academic Press, New York. P. W. ATKINS and K. A. MCLAUCHLAN (1972) in *Chemically induced magnetic polarisation* (editors A. R. Lepley and G. L. Closs). Interscience, New York.
^{13}C n.m.r. spectroscopy. E. F. MOONEY and P. H. WINSON (1968) *A. Rev. N.M.R. Spectrosc.* **2**, 153.
^{19}F n.m.r. spectroscopy. J. W. EMSLEY and L. PHILLIPS (1971) *Prog. nucl. magn. reson. Spectrosc.* **7**, 1.
^{31}P n.m.r. spectroscopy. E. G. FINER and R. K. HARRIS (1971) *Prog. nucl. magn. reson. Spectrosc.* **6**, 61; J. F. NIXON and A. PIDCOCK (1968) *A. Rev. N.M.R. Spectrosc.* **2**, 346 (coordination compounds).

Chapter 3

Transition metal ions. A. CARRINGTON and H. C. LONGUET-HIGGINS (1960) *Q. Rev. chem. Soc.* **14**, 427.
Inorganic radicals. P. W. ATKINS and M. C. R. SYMONS (1967) *The structure of inorganic radicals.* Elsevier, London.
Gaseous radicals. A. CARRINGTON (1970) *Chem. Br.* **6**, 71. Chemical Society, London.

Chapter 4

Theory of chemical shift. W. N. LIPSCOMB (1966) *Adv. magn. Reson.* **2**, 138; J. I. MUSHER. ibid. 177.
Hydrogen bonding. J. C. DAVIS and K. K. DEB (1970) *Adv. magn. Reson.* **4**, 201.
Rate effects. C. S. JOHNSON (1965) *Adv. magn. Reson.* **1**, 33.
Paramagnetic molecules. G. A. WEBB (1970) *A. Rep. NMR Spectrosc.* **3**, 211.
Paramagnetic molecules in structure determination. C. D. BRAY, A. C. T. NORTH, J. A. GLASEL, R. J. P. WILLIAMS, and A. U. XAVIER (1971) *Nature, Lond.* **232**, 237.
Biological applications of n.m.r. B. SHEARD and E. M. BRADBURY (1970) *Prog. biophys. molec. Biol.* **20**, 189.

Chapter 5

Theory of spin–spin coupling. J. N. MURRELL (1971) *Prog. nucl. magn. reson. Spectrosc.* **6**, 1.
Correlation of n.m.r. coupling constants with structure. S. STERNHELL (1969) *Q. Rev. chem. Soc.* **23**, 236.
Conformations of molecules from n.m.r. W. A. THOMAS (1970) *A. Rep. NMR Spectrosc.* **3**, 92.

Chapter 6

Double resonance. R. A. HOFFMAN and S. FORSEN (1966) *Prog. nucl. magn. reson. Spectrosc.* **1**, 15; heteronuclear double resonance. W. MCFARLANE (1969) *Q. Rev. chem. Soc.* **23**, 187.

Chapter 7

Spin labels in biology. C. L. HAMILTON and H. M. MCCONNELL (1968) in *Structural chemistry and molecular biology* (editors A. Rich and N. Davidson). Freeman, San Francisco.

Solid state e.s.r. J. R. MORTON (1964) *Chem. Rev.* **64**, 453. P. W. ATKINS and M. C. R. SYMONS (loc. cit.); M. C. R. SYMONS (1963) *Adv. phys. org. Chem.* **1**, 283.

Solid state n.m.r. R. E. RICHARDS (1956) *Q. Rev. chem. Soc.* **10**, 480. L. W. REEVES (1969) *Prog. nucl. magn. reson. Spectrosc.* **4**, 193.

Partially-oriented molecules. G. R. LUCKHURST (1968) *Q. Rev. chem. Soc.* **22**, 179; P. DIEHL and C. C. KHETRAPAL *NMR: basic principles and progress* **1**, 1.

Derivation of dipolar energy operator: C. P. SLICHTER or A. CARRINGTON and A. D. MCLACHLAN, loc. cit.

Index